THE
ULTIMATE
PROPHECY™

Book One

THE INITIATION

by

Moshé Zwang

Ultimate Mind Publisher, Los Angeles, California

Ultimate Mind Publisher
P.O.Box 7453,
Van Nuys, CA 91409-7453,
USA

Library of Congress Catalog Card Number: 95-80574
ISBN: 0-9645519-0-X

Book design: Diana Zwang
Illustration: Moshé Zwang

Dedication

I dedicate this book to the memory of my late father,
David Zwang.

Acknowledgments

I would like to thank my loving, gifted wife, Diana Zwang, who worked with me days and nights to help me present this important book sooner to humanity.

To Elizabeth Kimberlin, for her endless time and efforts in proofreading this book.

To Yaron Swery, for his support during the journey of bringing this work to print.

Also to my loving family, friends, students, clients, supporters and all the readers of my works, although not direct contributors to this book, nevertheless they are the very foundations for creating this and other works in my life.

GOD BLESS YOU ALL !

Contents

1
The Beginning

Strange . . . today is Friday, 3/3/95 and the order I have been filling all day has this number as well . . . 3395. What a coincidence . . .

Right there I knew. This coincidence was a sure sign that something good was about to happen, as it had always occurred in my life. But even this advance hint didn't prepare me for the coming events that have totally changed my life and eventually will influence the entire human population on Earth. It started the day I first met David.

* * *

The office room at my company in the San Fernando Valley, on the West side of metropolitan Los Angeles, California, was the same as usual. At 4:00 p.m., after a full day of intensive activity, I was tired, just waiting to finish the long day. I had a large order of various essential oils to fill, and being in my new business the president and the main worker at the same time, it made my day quite busy. The new warehouse worker, Jose, counted and packed every item in the list competently and quickly. Next, I had to check the packages, just to make sure before we send the cartons away. I couldn't afford to make mistakes, especially not with the first large order from a new customer.

I must succeed with it . . . an order like this, I get only once in a few months . . . hopefully, we can deliver this order today . . . within an hour or so, the truck should arrive for the special delivery . . . then I am free . . . I'm going to finish my work for the day . . . the other jobs can wait . . . as long as I send the merchandise on time, it seems like I'm OK in my mail-order business . . . If we can continue this way, besides selling my book, it's got a good potential for growth . . . I believe that in one year from now the business will double in size, then I can employ some more workers to help me . . . actually I need more help now . . . In addition to the new secretary, Joanna, and the warehouse worker, Jose, it would be nice to have another two workers in the warehouse, one aggressive salesperson in the marketing department and a personal secretary to do the accounting. That could make my life easier and at the same time help the company grow faster . . . but right now I can't afford that . . . We still have to grow into our maximum capacity . . . We haven't reached that point yet . . . not yet . . . maybe next year . . .

Soon I'm going home. Probably we'll take off tomorrow . . . go to Las Vegas for the weekend . . . or maybe drive up north to Monroe or San Francisco . . . Let's see what Diana, my wife, plans to do for the weekend . . . She deserves a vacation as well . . . She is so helpful . . . Just the thought about her gives me new energy . . . yeah, we are best friends, not just married . . . she is so wise, loving and supportive . . . and yes, so beautiful . . . Her beauty . . . always warms my heart . . . I can't wait to be back home . . . hug her for a long moment . . . and simply be with her . . . observe her pure, loving look while we talk . . . then . . .

All of a sudden the entrance door was opened. A stranger was standing by the door staring at me. There was nothing unusual in his appearance. A regular guy, about five feet, nine inches, darkish blond hair, bright blue eyes, wide shoulders, well-built, a little overweight, about one hundred and eighty pounds, wearing a white shirt and grey corduroy pants and regular black shoes. The guy was holding a pack of papers in his left hand. He simply stood there, waiting for me to invite him in. He didn't look like a salesman nor like a clerk. Let's see what he wants . . . I wondered.

But the moment I wanted to invite the stranger in, looking at him with a second glance, something was trembling inside me. My heart was pounding strongly. There was something in that man, some energy that when looking at him, sent goose bumps all over my body. I found myself totally alert. The room disappeared for a while. This person was shining, like having a strong aura surrounding his entire body, yet, there was nothing I could put my finger on. Is it my imagination . . . ? Is he a real person . . . ?

The stranger entered the office as if in slow motion. The whole world stopped moving. The room became brighter. Something was happening . . . I totally forgot the order, the work and even to breathe. It wasn't scary or dangerous, but as if I were in the middle of the highest ceremony on Earth, as if the room became special, cleaner, as if this were a special moment in my life, with no explanations, with no reason whatsoever to think that way.

The spell was suddenly broken when the stranger seated himself on the other side of my desk and started to talk with a heavy Hebrew accent. He was looking at me in a friendly way, as if I were an old friend of his. I had never seen this guy in my life. Yet, I felt he knew quite a lot about me, if I was to judge from the way he talked and his casual behavior.

"Hi, I'm David," he introduced himself. "And I know your name is Moshe. Yes, we are both from Israel. You don't know me directly, but I know you. Actually I know you very well."

I found myself again with goose bumps all over my body. His words somehow touched a very deep part of my mind, awakening some remote memories. It was nothing concrete, just deep feelings that I have somehow a connection to this person. I couldn't stop shaking as he continued.

"I want you to dedicate a few moments of your time to a

proposal I have for you. It is something that will change your life, but don't worry. It is a positive change." The stranger continued with a softer voice.

"I have nothing to sell and I don't ask anything in return for what I have to offer you. Yet, it is going to be the biggest venture you have ever entered into your life. The type of activity you have always dreamed about."

The stranger put on my desk the thick pack of papers he had been holding in his left hand. It seemed that the papers had been all handwritten in a fine blue ink. From where I sat, I could detect the rhythmic, normal handwriting size, but couldn't read the contents. Some of those papers were a little yellowish on the corners, indicating they had been exposed to the sun for a while or simply were old writings. Observing that yellowish pack, I wondered what those papers had to do with me.

The stranger smiled as if I were talking to him and soon he replied to my unspoken question.

"Moshe, in these papers my life story is unfolded, but this is just the minor part. In these papers I'm revealing the most well kept spiritual secrets on our planet. These are the true secrets of the spiritual phenomena; issues that the whole world should know about. These papers contain the true secrets of the Universe, the laws of Nature and advanced scientific information. These papers are written carefully, in such a simple way that the entire population on Earth will be able to read them. And once they read the content of these pages, they will pass it on to others. The messages here are so strong, that soon the entire planet will talk about the information unfolded in this manuscript, understanding the profound spiritual reality which will prepare humanity for the next evolutionary process on Earth.

"The great event, that the Divine Forces of the Creator have been waiting for so long, is going to take place soon, for the wellness and benefit of all human beings on our planet."

"But wait!" I interrupted, "Who do you think I am? I think you have the wrong person!" His high words sounded too weird to me for a moment. I suspected the stranger was a lunatic or a dreamer, although something very deep inside me knew: This person was carrying a real message.

"Moshe, believe me," the stranger replied, "I know about you more than you will ever believe, and, NO, I'm not a lunatic nor a dreamer. Within a few minutes you will know more about my offer.

"There is a reason that I have chosen you to publish this work. I don't ask anything in return. It is part of my mission in life to reveal this information, and then let the people of the planet Earth judge its authenticity and act accordingly.

"You, Moshe, are going to have the entire copyrights and the entire benefits of this work. You will be the only owner of the whole manuscript, and I want you to present yourself as the author of this work; as such, the whole thing is yours. It will bring you fame and money beyond your wildest dreams, but there is one condition: YOU CANNOT CHANGE THE CONTENT OF THIS WORK. You can design the pages, but absolutely no changes, even if the content seems strange. You can correct the English grammar, ask for proof reading, and make some illustrations, but do not change the text!"

"Wait a minute!" I protested again. "Who said I want any part of this manuscript? I'm too busy with my company, I have no time for your work. Besides, I'm not a publisher. And it's true, I have written three books, but those were in the alternative medicine field—never a story book."

That moment I knew I was wrong. I'm going to take that manuscript . . . but why? Why should I abandon years of investments for something that I don't even know . . . ? Is this what we call destiny . . . ?

Then trying to get the answers from the stranger, I looked straight at him. A shocking sensation passed through my entire body.

This stranger actually looks exactly the same as I do . . . exactly like myself . . . same appearance . . . same colors of hair, eyes and skin . . . the same way of talking with the heavy Israeli accent . . . No, it is impossible . . . such remarkable similarities . . . Is he my unknown twin brother . . . ? Am I dreaming?

Observing him, I felt a strange sensation. This person, a complete stranger a few moments ago, is actually part of my life, but how . . . ?

During that time the stranger was simply looking at me with a friendly smile, letting me struggle with my confused thoughts. Then he glanced at the manuscript he had just put on the desk, and casually picked up more than three-quarters of the pack.

"You know, Moshe," the stranger said in a soft voice, "it is too much for the beginning. You have here enough material for the first book." He pointed at the first part of the manuscript which he had left on the desk.

"Read it. I will be back here tomorrow at about the same time in the afternoon. Then we shall discuss it further. And please don't worry, just read it. Let's hear your opinion tomorrow. At the worst scenario, you will have the opportunity to read special spiritual information. OK?"

I was speechless. Looking down at the rest of the pile that was on the desk drew my curiosity now. What do I have to do with it . . . ? I wondered. Then raising my head, I was left all of a sudden with goose bumps again. THE STRANGER DISAPPEARED FROM THE ROOM AS IF HE NEVER EXISTED.

He couldn't have gone that fast . . . The desk is more than twelve feet away from the door . . .

Then out of curiosity, I quickly ran to the entrance. Looking outside, I saw no one there. The small street was quiet. No car nor any person was present at that moment.

Can't be! Even if a car was waiting for him outside, with a private driver ready to take off, it just would be impossible for him to disappear so rapidly . . . Strange . . . did I fall asleep . . . ? Maybe he did hypnotize me . . . ? But NO WAY! It is impossible. I am very familiar with hypnosis . . . there must be something else; maybe it is all an illusion . . .

I walked back into the building.

Jose welcomed me, tired but satisfied. "I'm done, boss."

"Thank you, Jose, have a nice weekend, and you too, Joanna." I acknowledged them, but they both gave me a strange look. I politely nodded my head and then quickly went into my office, closing the door after me.

Looking at the partial pack of the manuscript made it clear to me: That stranger, who called himself David, the same name as my late father, was a real person. Then without thinking twice, I grabbed that pile of papers and sat at my desk. Once I began reading, I just couldn't stop. The text was so fascinating, so simple, yet so powerful.

All of a sudden a knocking at the entrance door disturbed my reading. Looking through the window, I recognized the truck driver who came to pick up the merchandise. Quickly I gave him the packages and went back to my reading. The manuscript was powerful, touching the deepest parts of my awareness. It started from a naive description of a young boy. Then, gradually enlightened the most profound aspects of life in genuine simplicity, answering many of my innermost questions as it deeply awakened my whole being, filling me with intense energy vibrations.

The phone was ringing. Glancing at the window now, I realized that it was already dark. It must be Diana . . .

I picked up the phone.

"Diana?"

"Is everything OK, Moshe?"

"Yes, honey, but I have to finish reading something. It's important. I'll talk to you when I'm done. It will take a while, OK? Love you. Bye."

I hung up and kept reading. Eventually, I found myself at 2:00 a.m. leaning backward with the manuscript in my hands. Taking a deep breath, I knew then that my life had been changed! Changed for good! Being very familiar with the foremost spiritual and metaphysical writings, I knew: This manuscript contains such simple, yet amazing information that no one can afford to ignore it . . . This is the type of information that for sure can change and actually improve the planet's destiny . . . I was fascinated.

Then my doubts were rising again. But if this is such powerful information, how come he gave it to me? There are so many who are known as sacred people, much stronger and better equipped than I to publish such amazing, life-transforming information . . .

I couldn't hold myself and, once arriving home, with little explanation to Diana, I went to read the manuscript all over again as if it were the first time I had seen it.

At the second reading, I also focused on the life events of this person, David. They were very similar to my own life events as if I were reading my own life story. I was amazed.

This person, David, had the same high school education at a marine boarding school just as I had . . . he experienced a clinical death at a swimming pool, just as I did . . . and the same encounter with the being of light . . . How is it possible? I must meet with him again. . .

It was nearly 8:00 a.m., Saturday morning, when I finished reading the manuscript for the second time. By now, I felt very regretful that I had let him take the major part of the whole manuscript. What if he doesn't come back today?

The day went by like in a dream state. I set the alarm clock for 3:00 p.m., but I couldn't close my eyes. Staring at the ceiling, all of my thinking was focused on the content of the manuscript, completely forgetting about the weekend vacation and about the routine work, just anticipating the afternoon meeting with David.

Then I realized that I hadn't made any copy of these papers. What if it gets lost . . . ? I decided to take it with me to make a copy of it, just in case.

At about 4:00 p.m. I arrived at the industrial center and parked the car just in front of the entrance to my company. The place was quiet. No one seemed to be there. I carefully carried the yellowish papers in my hand and walked directly toward the door. Soon I was in. Then glancing at the desk in my office, I realized that there were some fax orders waiting for me. I was amazed. There were more than seven orders from companies which I had contacted a long time ago. How can it be? . . . on Saturday? It seemed a mystery to me. Is it possible that the manuscript has acted as a good luck talisman?

After making a copy of the manuscript, I sat at my desk waiting for the stranger.

Yesterday he was here a little after 4:00 p.m. . . . now it is already 5:00 . . . I hope he'll come . . . He had said he would be here at the same time . . . I'll wait for another half an hour . . .

Then just when I was about to leave, David, the stranger, appeared in my office.

"Moshe," the stranger looked directly into my eyes. "I know you have been reading the manuscript all night. Can you see now the importance of this work?"

"Yes, David, you are right, but this is only a part of it. I would like to read the rest of the manuscript before judging anything."

David just smiled and then in a softer voice said, "In due time, Moshe. Everything in life has its own timing. For now let's proceed my way."

"Moshe," David continued in a louder, more energetic voice, as if he had a lot of information to share with me, "remember the insights you had, those ingenious thoughts about creating a new therapy out of palmistry? Those thoughts that you had back in Israel? Let me remind you, at the end of the year 1985, a few months after you got married to Diana?"

"Who are you?" I was shocked.

The person in front of me just smiled with reassurance, ignoring my question.

"Do you remember, Moshe, the thoughts you had about the correlation between handwriting analysis which became graphotherapy, and then the thinking that maybe palmistry can become a therapy method as well? . . . your thinking about the brain, mind, soul and the hand connections?"

I didn't answer. In fact I did remember it quite well. I had just completed a book about this method—one which I named *Palm Therapy*. By now I was curious, and I wanted to hear more.

David smiled, then responded as if he just read my mind.

"Trust me, Moshe, I know you more than you know yourself, therefore you don't need to check me. Trust me. In due time you will understand."

"What really do you mean?" I was serious now.

This stranger can somehow read my mind. I cannot fool him . . . The manuscript content is real . . . Let's see what he wants from me . . .

David continued. "Those ingenious thoughts you had were actually implanted in you. The angel Lamdiel actually was helping you to develop this unique theory and therapy. It was done slowly, thus in order for you to take the coming steps and develop its full potential. It was done as part of your destiny. Can you understand? Nothing is really coincidental in life. There was a purpose for your ability to develop it and the game you just called: *The Zwang Board of Destiny*. You see, Moshe? Our mutual path precedes yesterday. The Divine Forces have been helping you for quite some time to develop yourself and your healing powers, so eventually you will be able to share your part for the benefit of humanity.

"Even the new seance board which you recently improved—yes, the one which you never have mentioned yet to anyone—is part of the insights which the angel implanted in you.

"Now, believe it or not," continued David in a low voice, "the whole purpose was to let you be stronger, so you will be ready to publish this manuscript. You will understand it much better after reading the last part of the whole manuscript. It isn't, however, the final one. It is very likely that from time to time, I will give you some more spiritual messages to publish. You cannot contact me, nor find me. You will understand why, after completing the reading of the entire manuscript. For now, I want you to work on this at every moment that you can and bring it to the public worldwide which has been superconsciously waiting for this information so many years.

"I will be seeing you," David continued, "but only from time to time. Now that you have finished the book *Palm Therapy*, start typing this manuscript. Remember: DO NOT CHANGE ITS CONTENT. The only changes you may make are corrections of English grammar and spelling. For the rest, leave it as it is."

I was totally in shock. I wasn't aware that there was so much influence on me when I had first thought about Palm Therapy and about my other innovations and inventions.

"Moshe, it is in your destiny to publish all of the Ultimate Prophecy Books, but don't worry, I will back you up and help you all the way because these spiritual messages are for the benefit of the entire humanity. It is a monument much greater than you and I together. It is the story of the Divine Powers in the Universe. It is given to humanity so that they can advance into the next cycle of evolution. You will read the other sections of it and then better understand the reasons. Eventually, the importance of this manuscript will be clear to you and to others."

With these words David slowly started to walk outside, then suddenly turned his head back toward me. "And one more thing, Moshe. A true spiritual message has the power to awaken healing vibrations into one's soul and also a need to inform the conscious mind by creating a signal that acknowledges its authenticity. Since, within this manuscript, there is real spiritual information, the kind that is intended to advance humanity, then it creates a major positive momentum that also will awaken the spiritual energy within the reader of the messages as long as that reader acts and lives within the positive evolutionary cycle as explained in the manuscript. You can challenge everyone on this sensation. Most people will sense vibrations or goose bumps once they hold the book on their left hand at the shoulder level.

I was fascinated. Is . . . that spiritual energy the reason that I feel so good and energetic today?

David only smiled and then slowly walked out while I was watching every step he made.

* * *

As soon as I got home, I started typing the Ultimate Prophecy, Book One—The Initiation:

2
The Near-Death Experience

I was fighting for air, breathing the same air from my mouth to my lungs in a closed circuit. I must get out of the water . . . No! Continue . . . continue . . . Yes, I must continue with my underwater swimming . . . but why? No matter what, I need to get out and breathe now . . . There is no more oxygen in my lungs . . . soon . . . soon I'll complete my task . . . then I can breathe . . . NO! NO! I MUST BREATHE NOW!

I jumped out of the water . . . and found myself sweating, breathing heavily on my bed . . . still fighting . . . with my blanket . . . sheet . . . and pillow . . .

My heart was pounding fast. The clock on the wall in front of me showed it was 5:30 a.m. I got out of my bed. My parents were still asleep. I pulled back the curtains of my room and opened the old wooden window. The fresh smell of summer plants filled the air. The open fields, extending out of our back-yard, were full of wild flowers, glowing with bright yellow and orange colors in the morning sun rising on Israel. I took a deep breath admiring the scene. A few birds were flying by, singing with beautiful rhythm.

None of my friends were here yet, but that wasn't a problem for me. I always found some entertainment, playing either with my construction game or with Regev, the neighbor's dog. That German shepherd was always ready to play with me. I used to throw a ball to a distance and he would jump and bring it back to me time and time again. The legend that he would tire anyone playing with him was not true, as the owner of the dog, Ruth, used to claim. If you are persistent, eventually the dog becomes so tired that he will refuse to play—a fact which I had proven to Ruth just the day before.

Ruth was about two years younger than I. She was eleven and a half years old, had long, smooth, blond hair, a round face and bluish, grey eyes. She was overweight and, in my opinion, very much spoiled.

Remembering yesterday's feast, I wondered if Ruth and her mother were still mad at me: . . . after all, she was the one who teased me with that wonderful box filled with my favorite chocolates . . . she refused to share it, not even one . . . yeah . . . I won the bet yesterday. Lucky for me that I didn't have to give her my watch . . . her dog was the one who fell down exhausted first—not me . . . I even offered that she should try encouraging him to continue the game . . .

I remembered how she had done so—initially with a sweet voice, then with anger, and eventually with tears. Then . . . after a few more minutes I, of course, had asked for my winning prize—the candy box.

Looking at the yard now, I recalled how she had handed it to me reluctantly. Yeah, I had offered her some, but she had been completely mad.

"You can have it all!" she had yelled.

Then, not thinking twice, I had run immediately to my secret place beneath a new house under construction. Within the next few minutes about one pound of special, creme-filled chocolate candies had gone; totally had disappeared into my stomach.

They were good . . . I thought while brushing my hair. Looking in the mirror, I remembered how I could hardly move my body when I had heard Ruth's mother saying in her loud, angry voice, "Don't worry, honey, we will catch that David and he will return all of your candies to you. Next time don't take the box to the street! Now, come after me!"

I recalled how, to my surprise, Ruth's mother whom I had known most of my life, had been aware of my hiding place.

Yeah, I could still hear her heavy footsteps approaching directly toward me. Next, how in a commanding voice (lucky for me she wasn't my mother) she had said, "OK, David, come out! Return the box to Ruth! You have no right to bet with her. She is younger than you, and you are not allowed to bet with her at all! Next time, if you want anything from Ruth, come to me!" Then. . . after five minutes of threatening, I had eventually crawled out with the empty candy box in my hands. Without a word, I had handed it to Ruth. Once she had taken it, apparently recognizing it was empty, she had started to cry again.

I recalled how her big mother had been silent for a moment. Then how she had screamed at me, "Where are the candies?" I had pointed to my stomach.

"You ate it all?" she had continued while observing my lean body with astonished eyes. Then, not saying an additional word, she had grabbed Ruth's hand and went back home.

Yeah . . . she could not believe that it had been the truth. I wonder if she is going to complain about it to my parents . . . It is not going to pass so quietly . . . maybe she did already . . .

The loud sound of a heavy garbage truck interrupted my thinking of the previous day's activities. I looked at the clock again. It was almost 6:00 a.m.

Why does time pass so slowly . . . I wish I could already be in the pool.

"Good morning David," my father said as he entered my room. "Son, I want to talk with you," he continued seriously. "Come. Sit here," he pointed to my bed, grabbed the wooden chair which was next to my desk, and sat in front of the bed. Then he looked at me for a moment with his penetrating, smart, blue eyes.

I held my breath. I was sure I knew the topic: No swimming for me today . . . But I was wrong.

As if he sensed that something was going to happen that

day, my father started to ask me about my activities in the swimming pool.

"What's wrong, Dad?" I finally asked.

"Well, nothing really, only your uncle told me that you are quite wild in the pool. Is it too boring for you there? You know I want you to be there to enjoy and practice your swimming skills. It is important for your physical development and this is why you are so muscular today. It will help you later in life. But, David, please don't be so wild there, and yes, stop the fighting games under the water. You may get hurt."

Strange . . . somehow his words seemed the continuation of my morning dream. "Yes, Dad" I nodded as my eyes were still opened wide anticipating the next questions.

"And besides," he continued, "these fighting games are not a good preparation for life. Those who have the need to fight all of the time are usually afraid of something, are you?"

"Mmmm, no," I responded, taking a deep breath, feeling better that the bet with Ruth was not mentioned. "All right Daddy, I'll behave." At that time I really meant it.

Soon the smell of fried eggs and fresh baked rolls filled my home. We went together to the kitchen. Breakfast was ready on the round table. My mother was still preparing herself for work. I couldn't eat much, neither could my father. Before he left, he gave me a big hug which showed me how strong he really was and how much he loved me.

My mother won't cause me much trouble if she finds out about yesterday . . . I know it . . . she usually doesn't say much when I so often misbehave. Only a sad look on her face, and a few minutes of moral talk—that would be the most. No problem . . . I can take it and then I will be free for the swimming pool . . .

Luckily for me, my mother didn't say much. Apparently, her good friend, Rachel, Ruth's mother, had not talked to her yet.

"Play safely. I'll see you in the evening. And don't forget

to clean up your room. It is too messy lately." She blew me a goodbye kiss as she rushed to the outside door.

"OK, Mom." My heart was pounding with joy.

Not a word about yesterday . . . Great, maybe Rachel will not make a big deal out of it . . .

Soon I locked the outside door and rushed to my bike. The day started to warm fast. I jumped on my bike and pedaled rapidly toward the swimming pool.

Fifteen minutes and I'm there . . .

A strange feeling crossed my mind in that morning of summer 1962 . . . It's going to be a very special day . . .

Seeing the huge gate of the swimming pool from a distance made me excited. That place, called the "Giant Wave," was like my second home. Fortunately for me, I had a free entrance to the pool because it was the property of my uncle, Abraham, an old, nice fellow whom I seldom saw to talk to. Soon I was there at the gate.

"Hey, good morning, David, how are you today?" the receptionist welcomed me with a big smile while opening the gate.

"Good morning, I feel great today," I replied and quickly parked and locked my bike at the same corner which was usually saved for me every day of the summer.

I looked around to see if any of my friends had arrived this early. The public swimming pool was a rectangular, Olympic-size pool of about 75' x 150'. It was built in the middle of five acres of recreation facilities. There were a few restaurants, an ice-cream parlor, a coffee shop, game arcades and great, green, open meadows. I could use all of these facilities for free, but I didn't waste my time. The water was more attractive to me than anything else.

After taking off my jeans and T-shirt in the locker room, I ran quickly toward the pool area. The same five old ladies were swimming there this morning, as usual, with their special old-fashioned caps, swimming glasses and some white cream on their noses. One of them pointed at me and quickly whispered something to her friends.

"Hello!" I waved to them.

They froze for a moment, and then, like a flock of geese, they turned together in the opposite direction and swam away to the other side of the pool.

What's wrong . . . ? I'm a good boy . . . maybe a little bit wild . . . so what if I jumped near them two days ago?

As usual, I then ran backward finding the best distance from the edge of the pool and, with a great speed, I dived into the water, creating that huge, powerful splash. I loved to swim under the water, occasionally touching the bottom of the pool. It was about fifteen feet deep in the deepest place. Early in the morning the water always felt a little bit cooler there. I swam under the water to the other side of the pool and then back. Getting some air, I was satisfied with the ease of swimming under the water a length of 150 feet in one breath. Next, with fast strokes of my hands and feet, I swam the width of the pool a few times, creating wild splashes of water all around me. As usual, the other few swimmers let me through. Then, feeling great from the vigorous exercise, I took some deep breaths and looked around for some adventures.

The pool area started to fill quickly. Some mothers were sitting on the striped couches enjoying the morning sun with their cute babies. The restaurants and the coffee shop were busy already, and the smell of fresh rolls, doughnuts and strong Turkish coffee filled the air.

I floated on my back enjoying the blue sky . . . not even one little cloud today . . . Next, I took a deep breath and in a second I was at the bottom of the pool. A small rock from the previous day's game caught my eyes. I happily picked it up. Then I rose from the water again, hoping to find someone to play with, but none of my friends had arrived yet, so I played by myself. I threw the rock upward in the air and immediately dived, searching after it. That was a game I really liked. Within a few moments, I was throwing the same rock again and again.

Soon the blowing of a whistle caught my attention. Looking backward, I encountered the angry eyes of Shula, the female lifeguard. She was a strong, big woman in her mid-thirties. She looked to me more like a man. I had heard that she had been an Olympic swimmer in her youth. I knew her from the many times she had threatened to take me out of the pool if I continued to misbehave. Somehow I had felt that although she had screamed at me several times, she actually liked me. She used to call me Fish Boy, "You stay in the water longer than most other people I know," she used to tell me with a smile. But I guessed that her patience was short at that moment.

"How many times do I need to ask you not to play this type of game? You almost hit that man in the brown bathing suit. You quit at once or you will not be allowed to enter the water again. Do you understand me, David?" she shouted in a furious voice.

I nodded, remembering the promise to my father just a few hours earlier. I felt lonely for a moment, but the water was inviting me to dive again.

Soon I found myself under a pair of white legs diving just above me. Who is she . . . ?

I guessed we both had the same question in mind since she immediately turned her face toward me. Beautiful . . . I thought, dropping the rock I had just found. We both jumped up to take some air. We looked into each others' eyes for a long moment without saying a word. She was really pretty; clear, blue, dreaming eyes, short, blond hair, cherry mouth and smooth silky skin. She was something. Her body was fully developed, yet athletic and soft.

"Hi, I'm David," I introduced myself, breaking the silence, "I live in the neighborhood, what about you?"

"I am Natasha," she responded with a lovely smile, revealing snowy white teeth, "We are new in this area and I don't know anyone in here," she added.

"Natasha is a beautiful name. How old are you?" I was hoping she was not much older than I.

"I'm fifteen years old. I just finished my grammar school and as from September I'll be starting my high school in Tel-Aviv. I lost a year of study because my family emigrated from Warsaw, Poland, about two and a half years ago, when my sister was born."

"Your Hebrew is great. I hardly can tell that you are a new immigrant. You must be an "A" student, aren't you?"

She lowered her eyes, then replied with a sad voice, "No, not really. I'm a bad student in math, Bible study and grammar. What about you?" she asked.

I guess I'm asking the wrong questions . . . How can I impress her? I wondered, while moving my fingers through my hair. "Well, what about me . . ." I repeated, ". . . I'm fourteen," I heard myself saying, increasing my age by a few months in order to sound old enough for her. "I love math and I think I can help you with it."

"It is OK. I don't need help in math. My father is a scientist and researcher in physics. He helps me, but I still hate math," she replied.

"My father is a scientist, too, in chemistry. He is a researcher of pharmaceutical new substances. Maybe they know each other." I immediately added, gladly, for finding something in common.

"Maybe," Natasha replied quietly. From the look on her face, I knew she didn't like the conversation, but she didn't leave me either. She kept looking at me with her beautiful, blue eyes.

"What do you like to do?" I eventually asked her, moving closer in her direction. "Do you like to see movies?"

"Oh yes," she nodded her head with a smile, "but now let's play a little, OK?"

"All right!" I said happily. "Let's take turns to see who can dive without touching the other. Here, I'll stand with open legs and every time you pass through without touching my legs you will win one point. If you do, by accident, then you lose one. OK?"

"Sounds good," Natasha replied.

We played for an hour, keeping the game's rule and counting the points. Then, gradually, we both started to lose one point after another.

"I like your light blond hair," she softly murmured.

The tension built up fast. We suddenly stood there in the water facing each other with anticipation.

"Do you have a girlfriend?" she asked me directly in a romantic voice. Then continued without waiting for my answer, "I had a boyfriend for a year and a half, but we separated in May, about two months ago. Now I'm looking for a new boyfriend, someone like you."

"Well . . . " I said, trying to hold myself together, "I don't have a girlfriend. I had one, but we separated last month."

By now my hands found hers under the water, and a source of warmth came from her.

"Your eyes are blue like the water," she said to me and put her face closer to mine.

In a few more minutes we found ourselves hugging each other passionately. I wasn't really an expert in these things. With my other girlfriend the only thing we did was talking and, at the most, giving a quick goodbye kiss on the cheeks or holding hands. But with Natasha I had a feeling that everything was OK. I could feel her physical attraction everywhere in my body. We were almost one unit in the water, touching each other body to body with such an intensity that I never had experienced before in my life. I had never thought it was possible to feel so much electricity in my body. Is this what's called . . . falling in love? I wondered.

Unfortunately for me, we heard a loud voice calling Natasha's name. I could feel Natasha's body stiffening. A big lady in her early forties, dressed in a long fancy towel dress came rushing toward the pool. She had short well-maintained blond hair, a wide face and heavy makeup. She seemed about to explode from anger. Oh no! Is this . . . monster her mother?

"Natasha, leave the pool immediately!" the big lady demanded.

Natasha didn't have much of a choice, but she held my hands tightly one more time. "Let's meet later, after my mother will calm down," she whispered. I nodded with my head, looking directly into her eyes as to keep her look in my heart. Then I looked toward her mother.

By now the face of Natasha's mother had gotten so hard and angry. She might never let us be together again . . .

I sadly watched Natasha leaving the water. Her mother was waiting impatiently next to the pool ladder. As soon as Natasha was out, the big lady grabbed her wrist and pulled her so as to make her walk faster. I kept following Natasha with my eyes. She had a perfect figure in her little pinkish bathing suit. Some deep, painful feelings passed through my whole body. I just started to have fun and that bitch is taking her away from me . . . I didn't do anything wrong . . . we both enjoyed wonderful moments.

Sadly I kept watching them walking toward the coffee shop. Natasha didn't dare to look back. The place was full of people already. She and her mother joined another grown lady who wore a big yellow hat, huge sunglasses and a grotesque, red bathing suit. They sat together at one of the round tables in front of the coffee shop.

The lady with the yellow hat looked familiar to me, but I wasn't sure from where. All of a sudden, I noticed a girl about my age exiting the coffee shop. She rushed toward that table and handed a large glass of orange juice to the lady with the big hat. Then turned and sat on the empty chair next to the three of them.

Oh no! That must be Rebekah and her mother . . . It seemed

they recognized me too, since they pointed in my direction. By now it was clear to me . . . Natasha's mother will never let me be with her daughter . . . I shouldn't have let Rebekah and her mother chase me in the water last week . . . but they didn't let me participate in the game . . . I then remembered how I had laughed and quickly disappeared with Rebekah's small ball. Yeah, with fast swimming strokes it had taken me only a few seconds to reach the other side of the pool, waving to them from there. "Wait until my husband catches you. He will teach you a lesson you will never forget," I could still recall her mother shouting furiously.

Well, I told myself, better forget about Natasha. You don't have a chance, David. All of them but Natasha looked in my direction for a brief second and immediately continued talking as if to confirm that I was the topic of their conversation.

Very soon I joined a group of kids playing "catch me" in the water. Being a fast swimmer, I liked that game. So, very shortly, I forgot about Natasha and the special feelings she had created in me. The game became much more important. Rebekah's mother apparently didn't have a husband, I concluded, because she never brought him to "teach me a lesson." I played with the boys for about two hours and I never looked back toward the coffee shop's direction where Natasha and her mother were sitting.

The sun, by now, was high in the sky. It was a hot, humid, summer day. Everyone seemed to be tired. At about 2:00 p.m. the game was naturally over. My good friend, Ben, swam toward me. He was a 14-year-old guy who looked more like a 16-year-old. He had black hair, dark skin and brown eyes, always smiling.

"Hey, David, I'm going to have some soda, do you want to join me?" Ben invited me.

"Sure! I am thirsty, too." But then something else caught my attention on the way out. On the west corner of the pool there was a gathering around a well-built man in his thirties. Apparently he was explaining something to a few of my friends, so I decided to swim over there. His name was Jacob, a tall guy of about six feet four inches. He had black hair and a tiny mustache. His eyes were dark brown and his teeth were yellowed, probably from a long time of smoking. His skin was dark and well-tanned. I could tell that he had spent most of his time in the outdoors. Everyone listened very carefully as he was explaining something about diving. I was curious. This is my area of expertise . . . I came closer to that man. He was holding a diving mask and swimming flippers in his hands.

"How long can you stay under the water without breathing?" one of my friends asked him.

"Well, I can swim under the water about twice the width of the pool," Jacob answered in his deep voice.

My friends stared at me. They knew I could do better. Somehow I felt I had to participate in this conversation.

"I can swim longer than that, maybe two and half widths or more."

"Well," Jacob asked, "can you swim under the water three times the width of the pool?"

"Yes," I replied without thinking twice. "I can do it!"

"Three times the width of the pool equals 83 yards (one yard equals 0.90 meter; 75 meters equals 83 yards). Are you telling me that you can swim this distance with one breath?" Jacob asked me in a cynical tone of voice.

I nodded.

"Yes, he can!" my friends supported me.

Jacob looked at me for a moment and then said, "I'm a professional diver, I never in my life saw a boy of your age and size who could, with one breath, swim under the water for that long distance without any equipment. You are the first one who claimed he can do it. Frankly, I don't believe it. Will you bet with me?" He then asked seriously.

"Sure," I replied immediately, although I never had swum

under the water three times the width of the pool. At the most I had swum twice and a little more of the width, but I figured, without thinking much, that with a little effort, I would be able to make it.

"What's your name, kid?" he then asked me.

"David."

"See these, David?" He raised his swimming equipment. "If you really can dive and swim under the water three times the width of the pool without taking your head out to breathe, it's yours. How about that?"

"Great!" I shouted, jumping with joy. This is my day. I'm going to win real swimming equipment. You, Jacob, are going to get the shock of your life, I thought, smiling happily to myself.

"Let's make an official bet," I offered to Jacob.

"What do you mean?" Jacob looked at me, amused.

"Let's give the equipment to a third party," I explained.

"Alright." Jacob smiled. And stared at a nice looking lady in her twenties who kept swimming very close to us.

"What about her?" he said.

"Fine with me." I replied.

Soon she was sitting next to Jacob with the equipment on her lap. My friends sat next to them at the edge of the pool.

"You can do it, David!" they encouraged me enthusiastically.

I started to prepare myself for the dive and long swim under the water, I was certain I would win. I couldn't even think about a defeat. It is a matter of willpower, nothing else. If you force yourself, you can do whatever you want, I told myself. Then I took a few fast deep breaths and expelled the air as much as I could. I repeated this procedure for a few times to guarantee maximum oxygen in my system. Then, after making sure that Jacob was watching me and the lady was holding the swimming equipment, I dived into the water, taking with me as much air as I could.

Somehow it started wrong. Maybe because of the excitement of the bet. I wasn't calm under the water as usual, but the first width of the pool went OK. I reached the side of the pool and touched it with my hand, then with a strong push of my legs, I turned to the other side and started the second width of the pool. It involved much more difficulties than I was used to. Nevertheless, I continued to the other side of the pool, being aware that my friends and probably all of the other swimmers are expecting me to make it. Maybe Natasha is watching me, too, I hoped for a moment. I finally completed swimming twice the width of the pool, but with the excitement I experienced, it felt harder than anytime before.

I can do it . . . I will continue to the other side and win . . . I must . . . I must finish and win . . .

I kept breathing the same air from my mouth to my lungs in a closed circuit. A sudden recollection of my morning dream crossed my mind . . . now it is different . . . I will . . . make it. . .

Gradually the air in my lungs seemed to be gone. Something in me wanted to get out urgently and have fresh air. But no . . . not me. If I get out now, it means I am a loser. It will never happen, I promised myself, and continued with strong, rhythmical, swimming movements of the hands and feet.

The need to get out of the water was urgent, but so was my need to reach the other side of the pool and win, therefore I continued.

Soon, I started to feel dizzy; my vision somehow blurred, but I continued with all my willpower. I won't get out . . . it is only another half of the pool, I tried to assure myself. I am the winner . . . this Jacob is losing his equipment today. I tried to smile under the water, but by now it seemed as if I had become too tired to think. All that mattered was to continue, to reach the other side.

Am I in the right direction . . . ? I started losing orientation of the other side. Suddenly the water seemed dark. My movements weakened tremendously, and tiredness started to take place. Continue ... continue ... you ... are ... going ... to ... win, I kept reassuring myself. Yeah ... I ... am ... going ... to ... make ... it ... only ... a few ... more ... feet ... and ... I ... am ... there ... Keep ... going ... You ... are ... strong ... David.

Then somehow it seemed to me that I was going to stop swimming, as if there was no more energy to continue swimming under the water.

"Air!" something was shouting in me, "Get out of the water and breathe NOW!"

No! I shouted back to myself. I am going to finish and win the bet!

Then as if that inner voice calmed down, I felt as if my mind were falling asleep. I continued to swim with no idea where I was or how much I still had to swim under water in order to reach the end. At some point during that painful struggle, it suddenly became immaterial. No more battling with the water. I somehow hoped that I was still swimming toward the end to touch the side of the pool, but I was totally indifferent by now. I felt like I was dreaming, but slowly continued to swim, or at least I thought so while entering into a strange, deep, unconscious sleep.

Then, all of a sudden, something amazing happened to me. I totally woke up. Somehow I was flying—no weight. I became very alert and refreshed, feeling as if I were vacuumed upward with a great velocity. It took a split second. The experience was so intense and so clear. I was astonished. No . . . this is not a dream! Something was pulling me out! What is happening to me? I could not figure it out at all.

It all happened so rapidly. I felt like I was flying at an enormous speed through a long and dark pipe that was also soft and secure. It didn't have real sides, but at the end of the pipe I could see a bright light. Suddenly I found myself out there, in the air, but in a unique position—I was actually floating in the air, about twenty feet above the swimming pool. Looking down was amazing to me. How can it be? I looked around . . . yes I'm floating in the air . . . but I have no fear of falling down . . . and . . . I don't feel my weight at all.

Within a few seconds it wasn't strange for me to float in the air anymore. Actually, it was very pleasant and peaceful. Although it was a hot humid, day, it felt totally different now—nice, warm and just right. The daylight seemed brighter, but also softer. Everywhere I looked, I could see clearly. The haze in the air was not blocking the horizon anymore. I felt as if some curtains were lifted, and I could observe the view easily.

Suddenly, I focused my attention down toward the side of the pool. It was incredible. My body, yes, my own body was lying there on the slab near the edge of the pool, and I—the same I—was out of my own body. What's going on? It astonished me. I kept looking down. Shula, the lifeguard, was working on my body, giving me mouth to mouth breathing, and pressing on my chest region every couple of breaths. My friends were gathered around my body. Ben was there as well. They were all frightened, observing my body without saying a word.

"Hey guys, nothing happened to me," I screamed happily, but none of them looked in my direction.

Then I noticed, Jacob, the diver with whom I had made the bet. He was biting his lower lip. I could read his mind, blaming himself for what had happened to me. Funny . . . he thinks I am dead . . .

I tried to relax him, "Hey, Jacob, I am alive, up here, it's me, David," I shouted, but he didn't hear me.

Then I focused my attention on the lifeguard, Shula. Another adult, whom I didn't know, joined her and immediately began pushing rhythmically at the central region of my body. Only then did I understand that actually they were trying to pull me back into my body

"No! Stop! Don't pull me back! It's great here!" I shouted with all of my power, but they apparently couldn't hear. They totally ignored the real me. "Forget it! I'm not going down! I'm staying up here!" I continued screaming at them.

Meanwhile, the crowd was growing. "Oh my God," I heard from every corner. I realized that most of them were just curious. They were not really sorry about what had happened. Somehow it disappointed me. Although I felt great, I expected people to be more concerned about someone who had just passed to the other side of life while in the water.

All of a sudden I saw Natasha. She stood there about thirty feet away from my body. I could see the tears in her eyes and felt the immense pain in her heart. I tried to communicate with her, using all of my power, "Natasha, don't cry. Look here! I'm up here! That guy on the slab is not the real me; it is only my body," I shouted, but it seemed as if she could not hear me either. I felt as if I were talking to deaf people. It was frustrating.

On the other hand it was wonderful. I could hear and see perfectly and clearly from any distance. Next, I realized that Natasha's mother and Rebekah's mother were rushing toward Natasha. They grabbed her wrists and then hastily made their way through the crowd.

"See? I told you to stay away from that boy. I was right. He is only a troublemaker," Rebekah's mother exclaimed in a nasty voice.

It really upset me. I noticed that Rebekah was waiting for them a few feet away from the crowd. Soon the four of them were heading outside, toward the exit gate, taking Natasha home.

I looked at my body again. It had just started to be fun floating in the air while I was resisting the attempts to pull me back down. Then I turned to look around. All of a sudden I could see other people floating just like me. They observed me with no attempt to come closer. I remained floating above my body. It felt great. Now I wanted to move but didn't know how, so I decided it was safer to stay where I was.

After a few seconds, I noticed that a huge and powerful person was floating by my side. He was a real giant, about nine or ten feet tall. He looked different from all of the other floating people. I could feel his enormous, powerful radiation of energy and yet he was not scary at all; more like a big father with a lot of love and care for me. He was shining as if he were illuminated from within.

Observing him carefully, I realized that he was made out of light. He didn't look solid but more like a cloud with an inner type of light within himself. Nothing definite to him. Yet, he had the figure of a real person, only huge, with a nice looking face. But whether a male or female—I couldn't tell. I assumed he was a male, just the feeling, but nothing was certain.

Then, all of a sudden, he commanded with a loving voice, "David, you must go back. It is not your time yet. There are many duties you must complete before coming here. Don't worry, you will be back here in due time. Now prepare yourself to go back."

"No!" I refused, "I want to stay here! I'm staying!"

The feeling was so good up there that I couldn't even imagine going down. By now I also became aware of light, soft music. It was a type of soft sound in the air, one which didn't interrupt my ability to listen to that huge person made out of an illuminated cloud.

I looked again to the being of light. Somehow I felt close to him similar to the way I feel toward my father.

The huge shining person continued to speak now with a soft voice, smiling, radiating enormous love as he did. I wanted to stay there, near him, forever and ever. But again I could hear his deep, gentle voice as if it came into me directly from him.

"David you must go down. It is not your time yet. David, the angels know that you are about to do great things for the world, but now you must return to your body."

"NO!" I responded stubbornly, "I'm not going back!"

Looking around, I noticed that the other people who floated nearby were smiling at me with loving and understanding looks on their faces. They, too, were made of strange clouds made of light, but not so intense as that of the huge person near me. It seemed to me as if he were much stronger, maybe the leader or higher authority. The being of light looked at me now with penetrating shining eyes. "We the angels, are going to be in touch with you soon, but now, get down!"

Is . . . he an angel?

Suddenly he got serious. Somehow I understood that I really had to go back. I looked down. Shula, the lifeguard, was really working hard, and the person whom I didn't know was still pushing into my chest. They were both sweating profusely. I felt their anxiety especially that of Shula.

"Don't worry I'm OK, Shula," I tried to calm her, but still resisting the going back. Then, looking ahead, I saw that the big wall clock next to the dressing rooms showed it was 2:28 p.m. Next, looking toward the sun, I noticed that actually the whole world was filled with a bright light in addition to that of the sunlight. It was amazing. I wanted to see more . . . but then, in spite of my resistance, I suddenly felt as if I were vacuumed down, falling rapidly right into my body.

It was a jolt and a shock for me. I slowly opened my eyes. I was angry.

"Thank God! He is alive," Shula shouted, crying. Then she hugged me tight and gave me a big kiss on my cheek.

"He is alive! David is alive!" I heard the crowd repeating. My friends held my hands.

"David, we were worried about you so much." Ben was laughing with tears, "I thought you were coming to drink a soda with me, and when I came back they told me you had died," he wiped his tears quickly.

I just laid there and listened for a while, reassuring them with my eyes. "Did I make it? Did I win the bet?" I finally asked.

"Yes you did!" I heard Jacob's choked voice from behind my back.

"Yes, you won David," added Gabby, who was one of the witnesses to the bet. "You actually reached the end, and then to our surprise you kept staying under the water. We were sure you had decided to prove to us that you could stay even for a longer time without any air. Only Shula noticed that something was wrong and rushed to take you out of the water."

Jacob handed me the swimming equipment. "It's yours, David. You really won it. Thank God you are alive. You scared me. I will NEVER bet with children again! NEVER!" He was nervous, cleaning the sweat from his forehead.

I could only smile. For me it was not traumatic at all. It was a great adventure. But somehow, I didn't feel like telling anyone about my experience. No, no one will care anyway and . . . Shula, the lifeguard, may get angry at me for resisting the return.

Suddenly the loud siren of an approaching ambulance was heard. Soon two men wearing white uniforms rushed toward me. One of them was very tall. The other not.

"How is he Dr. Goldshmit?" they both asked the man who had been working on my chest.

"He was drowned. When the lifeguard pulled him out of the water, there were no signs of breathing or heart function. It seemed to me that he had a clinical death. We had to perform CPR. It wasn't easy. We almost lost him." The doctor looked seriously, and then added, "He seems OK now, but he'd better be checked in the hospital, just in case."

"I'm OK," I quickly interfered.

"Are your parents here?" the tall guy in the white uniform asked.

"No, he usually comes by himself," Shula answered, patting my head.

"We will need to take him to the nearest hospital," the tall guy continued.

"I'll join you!" Jacob announced.

"No, it's OK, Jacob," I thanked him. "Just keep the equipment for me until tomorrow."

"Yeah, we will take care of him," the tall guy assured them.

"Let me get his clothes real quick." Jacob removed the tag from my wrist and soon came back rapidly with my jeans and T-shirt.

"I'm OK, see?" I said loudly while carefully standing on both legs. But somehow it seemed difficult. I felt weak and tired.

Abruptly I found myself lying down on the bed of a rushing ambulance. The siren was on. I stared at the ceiling of that vehicle, remembering, again, the promise to my father early that morning. Did I break my promise to him? No, I decided. I didn't do anything wrong. I was OK most of the day. The only thing I hoped was that no one would tell my parents about what had happened to me in the pool.

Within less than ten minutes I was in the hospital. The place was huge. It felt cold inside. Soon I was examined by a doctor.

"Hi, my name is Doctor Cohen," he introduced himself.

"It seems that you're doing all right," he concluded after a short physical check.

"Can I go back to the swimming pool now?" I was happy.

He looked astonished, raising his eyebrows. "No, we will drive you right home. You need some rest today."

"There," I told the hospital driver, pointing toward the white apartment building.

I reached the keys in my pocket and opened the door. I was lucky. My parents were not home yet. The driver handed me the medical report and left.

After drinking plenty of orange juice, I went out and stood in the front yard thinking what to do next. Should I go back to the pool . . . ? Can I walk . . . ? It will probably take me less than an hour to get there . . .

The day was still hot and the sun was hitting the west wall

of the building. It was quiet. A few large, white butterflies were flying near me. How beautiful these little creatures are . . . I was floating in the air a few hours ago, just like them . . .

"Mom, David is back!" I suddenly heard Ruth screaming from the balcony of the second floor.

"I'm sure he could not have finished all of them. Maybe we can have him return the rest of the candies to you. He probably hid them in one of his secret places," her mother yelled back from inside their apartment.

Oh no, not now . . . I just had enough time to escape into our apartment through the open balcony on the first floor. The best way is to stay away from them until the evening . . . then they might give up or understand that it is too late to ask for the chocolate candies . . .

I lay down in the patio in our backyard, hidden from Rachel and her daughter Ruth. I stared at the blue sky. I could still hear them talking about me, but somehow it didn't bother me anymore. Something strange had happened to me. My priorities had changed. I lost interest in the games I used to create, as if there were something much more exciting in life for me than the teasing of others and my greatest everyday adventures which became altogether meaningless. I felt missing it terribly the few fantastic moments of being up there, floating up in the sky. Those moments had been so powerful for me that they were surpassing any other experiences in my life so far. Remembering how great it had felt up there, I slowly closed my eyes and fell asleep.

I don't know for how long I slept in the patio. But when I woke up, there was only one thought in my mind—visiting the other side again.

3
The Proof through the Seance Board

Yes, I must get back there . . . I know I will, one way or the other . . . but how? Is there . . . any other way, besides the one I had in the swimming pool? That I didn't know.

Trying to make myself to experience a near death again is not an appealing solution . . . The huge being of light I met there will probably send me right back, just as he did this time. Why are all the fun things forbidden . . . ? Can I go back to the floating side . . . ?

But, then, remembering the painful moments before it had happened, I didn't want to suffer in the water again. I just wanted to reexperience those great moments and the exciting feelings I had had up there.

I sensed that I wouldn't get help from anyone I knew, especially not from my family . . . This issue will not be a welcome subject . . . Yeah, I was aware of their approach to life and safety issues. No . . . they won't help me, I concluded. They will be angry with me . . . So how shall I find the way out of my body . . . ?

All of a sudden I jumped up. Yes, I know! Leo! I screamed with joy. Then, after leaving a short note for my parents, I was out marching rapidly the long way toward Leo's house.

Leo was one of my classmates. He was not a really close friend of mine, but I had heard that his nice, 24-year-old sister, Debra, regularly performed a type of communication with spirits through what he called a "seance board." I had never participated in one of these types of communication and, prior to my passing to the other side of life, I never had believed it was real. I simply had accepted the "scientific" explanations of my father's friend, Dr. Ron, a highly respected psychiatrist. "There are no such things as spirits; it's an illusion of the mind. The ones who move the glass on the seance board are the participants themselves operating it with their subconscious minds. No spirits are involved!" he used to say with his authoritative voice.

Until that morning I could still accept his theory as the true reality together with the other "logical" explanations of my parents about those issues, but, now after what had happened to me in the pool, I knew he either was wrong or had lied to me. But why? Are all the grownups hiding this subject from kids? Maybe the same as they avoid discussing sex? I wondered, hoping that Leo knew more about those secrets.

I walked for an hour, crossing the wide, open fields. Finally I recognized Leo's house from a distance. The sun already had set well below the horizon, and a round, white moon hung there above the tall eucalyptus trees. The neighborhood was quiet, only the howling of the jackals was heard in the distance. A gentle sea breeze from the Mediterranean filled the air. I took a few deep breaths and continued to march.

Getting closer to the house, it seemed that the place was busy. Many cars were parked in front of it and all the lights were on.

Oh no, I've probably arrived at the wrong time. They must be having a party tonight . . . but maybe it is his parents' party . . . so Leo will be free to chat with me.

I knocked on the brown door, but no one opened it, so I rang the bell.

"Hi David! What are you doing here? Come in," Debra welcomed me with her warm voice.

"I need to speak with Leo. Is he at home?"

"He'll be back shortly. He just went to bring some soda

from the grocery store. Feel at home," she continued.

"Are you having a party tonight?" I carefully asked.

"No," she responded and pointed to the people who were in the living room. "These are just a few of my friends who came here to have an evening of communication with spirits. We call it a seance."

I held my breath. "Debra . . . can I join your seance? I won't disturb your party. I promise. I'll sit quietly . . . in a corner. I must see a real seance. OK Debra? Please!?" I continued with great intensity.

"You know, David, we never let kids around when we perform a seance, but we have a law that anyone who asks to participate, we let him do so, because it is his own karmic responsibility.

"Now, do you really want to participate?" she asked me seriously, looking directly into my eyes.

"Yes!" I nodded quickly. My excitement grew rapidly. I wanted to jump from happiness, but I controlled myself. On the other hand I wasn't really surprised. Somehow I had known she would agree.

"You can have a seat there, by the window, David." She pointed at one of the wooden chairs that were placed together against a white drapery. Then she smiled at me and went to talk with her guests.

I sat there quietly, observing everyone. The room was full of people. Most of them were in their early twenties. A few of them sat down on the cream sofa along the wall, and the others stood by the round wooden table in the center of the room. They all looked very excited and serious, taking turns sharing their experiences. I tried to follow. Maybe . . . I'll learn from them more about getting back . . . to the other side.

To my disappointment, they mentioned concepts with which I wasn't familiar; terms like "mediumship," "sixth sense" and "healing energy."

A couple who sat silently on the minisofa to my side noticed my interest and looked at me with understanding smiles. Soon the door bell rang.

"It must be Leo," Debra said and hurried to open the door. "Did you find some more candles, too?" I heard her asking.

"Yes," Leo replied and handed the packages to her, as he walked in.

"David is here. He'll join the seance tonight," she said pointing to me.

I stood up waving to him, "Leo,"

"Hi David, good to see you. What's up, buddy?" He was surprised to see me there, walking toward me with a questioning look on his face.

I took him to the corner of the room, "I wanted to learn more about this stuff. Is it OK with you if I stay for the seance?" I needed his acceptance, just in case Debra would change her mind.

"Debra agreed, then there is no problem at all, David." He replied. "But if you get bored, you can join me. I'm going to read some comic books in my room." he continued.

"Thank you, Leo, I appreciate it."

"Do you want some soda? I just bought some"

"No, thanks, Leo, I'm not thirsty."

The smell of burning candles suddenly filled the room. Debra appeared there holding two burning candles in her hands. Another nice looking girl with a ponytail followed her. She held a large white cardboard and a transparent glass cup.

"They are about to start. I'll see you later." Leo whispered and quickly disappeared.

The lights in the house were turned off one after the other. The two candles and the board were placed on the round table. I raised my head to see better. That must be the seance board, I speculated with a thrill.

Debra and the girl with the ponytail sat down at the table, not saying a word. Two guys and another girl with long, dark, curly hair joined them silently. The girl carried a large note-book and a pen. Looking at the way we sat I noticed that two circles were formed. I was in the outer one; the only kid in the room. The five around the table held hands and closed their eyes. After a few seconds of silence which for me seemed like hours, Debra and the girl with the ponytail placed their fingers on the glass which was laying on the board. The two guys who sat at the table did the same.

"May the spirit come in?" Debra asked in a deep voice.

They all looked very serious. Everyone's attention was focused on the board. Suddenly the glass started slowly to move round and round. I didn't remove my eyes from that glass. I could see clearly that actually Dr. Ron was right. The four people were moving the glass fast to different locations on the board stopping for a moment on a specific letter and then continuing to the next one. I was disappointed. No spirit was moving the glass. I continued to observe them carefully. The girl with the curly hair quickly followed the fast movements of the glass and took notes simultaneously. Suddenly the five of them stopped and looked at each other.

"The spirit is asking the person who returned from the dead today to please come closer to the table," the curly-haired girl announced.

No one moved. It didn't mean much to me. Everyone was looking for that guy who returned from the dead, and I, too. Yes, I was curious to meet him myself.

"Please, we don't have the whole night. The one who came back from the dead knows it. So please, come, don't be afraid." The curly-haired girl added.

Again, I was looking around as everyone else did, but no one volunteered to move forward. Only the white drapery behind me moved slowly backwards and forwards with the evening breeze, patting my head occasionally.

All of a sudden, the glass on the table moved again. Everyone followed it carefully.

D..A..V..I..D, the board spelled my name. I shook a little.

C..O..M..E F..O..R..W..A..R..D D..O N..O..T B..E A..F..R..A..I..D

We all looked at each other again. There must be another guy by the name of David in the room, I calmed myself, remaining silent. Besides, I was just a guest who promised to be quiet and not to disturb in any way.

"Wait a minute," Debra shouted and turned her head toward me.

"David, come here!" She pointed to the table.

I slowly walked toward her. Are they joking on my account...? I suspected. "Listen, maybe I'm only a kid but I'm not stupid," I quickly announced.

Debra's face turned very serious.

"David, do not offend the spirit!" she commanded.

"It's serious! We are not making fun of you. The spirit wrote it," the guy next to the curly-haired girl added.

I stood there silently for a second. Then I looked at the board and exclaimed, "OK, if you are for real, then how much money do I have in my right pocket?"

A sigh was heard from all the participants in the room.

I, myself, didn't know how much money was there. It wasn't much, but enough to test the board.

The glass moved faster now:

Y..O..U A..R..E S..T..I..L..L Y..O..U..N..G D..A..V..I..D A..N..D W..E U..N..D..E..R..S..T..A..N..D Y..O..U..R S..K..E..P..T..I..C..I..S..M Y..O..U H..A..V..E S..I..X..T..Y E..I..G..H..T G..R..U..S..H (similar to cents) I..N Y..O..U..R R..I..G..H..T P..O..C..K..E..T

I slipped my right hand into my right pocket and quickly summed up all the little coins. Everyone followed with anticipation, fifty . . . sixty . . . sixty-five . . . sixty-six, sixty-seven, sixty-eight. Exactly! My heart was pounding rapidly.

The glass moved again.

N..O..W D..O Y..O..U B..E..L..I..E..V..E M..E?

"Yes," I responded, still shaking, "but I wasn't dead to-day."

Y..O..U W..E..R..E O..U..T O..F Y..O..U..R B..O..D..Y
I..N A C..O..N..D..I..T..I..O..N W..E C..A..T..E..G..O..R..I..Z..E
A..S B..E..I..N..G A..M..O..N..G T..H..E D..E..A..D
P..E..O..P..L..E

I became the center of attention now.

The board continued:

Y..O..U S..T..I..L..L H..A..V..E A L..O..T T..O
L..E..A..R..N B..U..T Y..O..U W..E..R..E S..A..V..E..D F..O..R
A R..E..A..S..O..N Y..O..U H..A..V..E A M..A..J..O..R
D..U..T..Y T..O P..E..R..F..O..R..M O..N E..A..R..T..H S..O
K..E..E..P Y..O..U..R M..I..N..D O..P..E..N T..O T..H..E
M..Y..S..T..E..R..I..E..S O..F L..I..F..E O..N..E D..A..Y Y..O..U
W..I..L..L N..E..E..D T..H..E..S..E S..K..I..L..L..S

The glass didn't move anymore.

I stood near the table shivering, with goose bumps all over my body. Something inside me was trembling without being able to control it. I crossed my arms. It was cold. I was still in the same light T-shirt and jeans which I wore after the incident in the pool. Debra noticed my trembling and hugged me. Then she left the room and quickly returned with a sweater.

"Here, David," She said softly, "This will keep you warm."

I sat down on the nearest chair. The lights were back on. Soon I found myself surrounded by all of Debra's friends. They asked me about my experience that day. I was very short about it, telling them that I had fainted in the pool, but never mentioned the passing to the other side, the floating above my body, or the spirits who were there with me. No, it's too much . . . and besides, they won't believe me anyway . . .

After a few more minutes, I realized it was already 10:00 p.m. "It must be late for the boy," someone said.

A couple suggested that they would drive me home. I gladly accepted their offer and told them how to get there.

We took the short cut through the dirt road crossing the fields. Rocking in their open roof Jeep, I looked up to the stars above. The night was enchanting. The fresh smell of the dry dirt mixed with the evening summer mist filled the air. In the distance the howling of the jackals could still be heard, somehow more clearly now. I was quiet all the way.

We arrived at the apartment building. The lights on the first floor were on. I then realized that I had totally forgotten to call my parents as I had written to them in the short note.

"Thank you," I said to the couple as I jumped out of the Jeep.

"Do you want us to walk you in?" the lady inquired.

"Oh no, I'll be fine."

"Alright, David, have a good night."

"Thanks. Good night." I waved to them as I quickly walked to my home.

I carefully knocked at the door.

My mother and father stood there looking at me very seriously. But, then without comment, they sent me to my bedroom. Feeling exhausted, I immediately fell asleep until late the next morning.

4
In Search for Ways Out of My Body

$\mathcal{S}$taring at the ceiling, I stayed awake in my bed that morning, reexperiencing in my mind the amazing time in which I had been floating peacefully in the sky just above my body. The memories of the spirit of light who had talked to me there were so vivid.

He promised that the angels would be in touch with me . . . but when? Was the spirit who communicated with me through the seance board one of them?

A quick look at the wall clock showed it was 11:00 a.m. Impossible! It's almost noon. I will arrive late at the pool today . . .

I sat up slowly on my bed. It was hard to ignore the memories of yesterday's experiences, but my stomach indicated that it was about time to get up and eat something. My parents were already at work. Glancing at my desk, I found a note from them. It read:

"Good Morning, David. Breakfast is in the kitchen. Please stay safe. Love, Mom and Dad."

I placed the note back on the desk, wondering if they had gotten a full report of yesterday's event. I really hoped they hadn't.

After getting dressed I went to the kitchen. A big breakfast was ready for me there. The scrambled eggs were cold, so I put them in the oven for a few minutes. Starting to eat, I realized how hungry I was. I took the last bite from the fresh baked roll and tried to plan my activities for the day. Nothing exciting crossed my mind. Everything I considered felt dull, empty

now. What's going on with me . . . ? I opened the refrigerator
. . . Let's see what's for dessert today . . .

Looking at my favorite cheese cake, I took a knife and a
clean plate, and then cut a big piece. I tasted the cake. It was
good but not enough. Next, I opened the freezer. A few scoops
of vanilla and chocolate ice cream should fix it . . . then some
chocolate syrup and lots of whipped cream on top . . . not forgetting a handful of cherries for "decoration."

I sat there at the table, looking at the colorful mountain on
my plate. Soon I was enjoying it not only in my mouth but
with my heart. My stomach became full and heavy, but nothing stopped me from indulging myself until the last spoonful.

Removing the dishes from the table, the emptiness feeling
I had felt earlier grew now. What shall I do next . . . ? The
memories of yesterday's conversation with the being of light
occupied my mind. I felt that I was missing the floating side of
life. I wanted to be back there, feeling as if I belonged there
more than here. Somehow I had known the other side of life
for a long period. I couldn't explain how, nor make much sense
to myself, but deep inside me, I felt that my real home was in
the other side of life, in that special lighted world which I had
just visited yesterday. I was confused. Even so, there was a
powerful feeling of knowing: the other side was another dimension of my real life.

How can I go back there . . . without passing through all of
the initial painful moments? . . . without having to go through
the struggle of not breathing until passing into the other side
at the end of the tunnel? I didn't have any answer to that. There
must be a better way . . . an easier one than the one I had gone
through . . . I can't discuss it with my own parents. They are
well-educated people. My father is a doctor in biochemistry,
and my mother an M.B.A. in business administration. She
works for a huge manufacturing corporation of medical de-
vices . . . but no, they can't help me . . . I have always trusted
my parents and received answers to many of my questions,

especially from my father who has a wide experience of life and is very knowledgeable in many areas . . . but no, not in this case. They are totally detached from spiritual issues . . . or maybe . . . they just avoid discussing them in front of me? Both of them are atheists . . . don't believe in God . . . nor in any religion or ritual. For them religion of any kind is a false and useless activity. Yeah . . . they call it, in a negative way, "spiritual manipulation." No . . . I can't get any help from them on this issue.

Feeling my throat choking from frustrations, I decided then to call Debra. She should know more. After all, she was the one who talked with the spirits last night. Definitely she is the one to be consulted.

I picked up the phone.

As I was dialing Leo's telephone number, a thought which was more like a clear inner voice said, "She is not going to help you David." By now, that voice had become a clear sensation of knowing, which was stronger than logical speculations. I decided to ignore that inner voice and be more logical. I also had a good excuse to call her—I needed to return the sweater.

"Hello"

"Hi, it's David"

"Hi, David. How are you? Do you feel better after yesterday's adventures?" Debra inquired with a warm, loving voice.

"Well, I don't know, really," I replied honestly. I felt an urge to ask her directly how to get into the floating side of life, but something in me prevented it. Was it shame or me being an introverted personality as I was diagnosed by my father's friend, Dr. Ron? No, it was something else . . .

It was somehow clear to me that although she made connections with spirits, she would refuse to discuss the issue with me like all other adults I had known so far. My thoughts carried me away . . .

"David, are you still there?" I suddenly heard Debra's voice from the other end.

"Yes," I hesitated for a second and then continued, deciding to ignore my thought about her.

"Debra, can I ask you something?"

"Well, sure," there was a little bit of surprise in her voice.

". . . Debra, how can I go back and visit the other side?" I finally asked her.

"What do you mean?" She raised her voice now.

"Well . . . you know. I want to visit the floating world."

"David, what are you talking about . . . ?" She was holding her breath.

"Well, I . . . just was wondering if you could help me go there again for a little while, you know, a visit to the spirits' side. "I tried to explain it in a different way, not making a big deal about it.

By now it seemed to me that she clearly understood, but to my regret, a terrified voice was heard on the other end.

"Oh my God!" she whispered, breathing rapidly now into the phone. "Do you want to die?" Her voice was weak and shivering now.

"No." I answered honestly. "That is not what I meant. I only want to visit the other side, you know, the floating side, only for a short while and then come back." I tried to be more reasonable and explain exactly what I wanted. She should know how to get out . . . She can talk to the spirits, therefore she could get their instructions as to how to visit the floating side of life, it is that simple . . .

There was a complete silence on the other end of the line. Apparently I was missing something in my communication with her. Did I offend her? Well, I guessed so, because she wasn't very friendly to me anymore.

"I think you should consult with a psychotherapist. You may need some help, David," she responded with a determined, sharp voice.

Somehow I felt as if she were actually talking to herself, totally ignoring my question.

". . . but Debra," I tried again, "I don't want to die, and besides, you don't really die when you leave the body. People are lying when they say so. I know it for sure. Adults lie to children."

I did my best to reason with her, but what I had just said was even worse. She sounded horrified by now. Somehow I could feel her insecurity. I realized that my inner voice was right. It was impossible to get answers or instructions from her.

A strange feeling crossed my mind. Only yesterday I had viewed the twenty-four-year-old young lady as an adult, with knowledge, wisdom and experience but, all of a sudden, I felt that she was actually a frightened kid. She was helpless. Never before had I viewed any adult as needing my help, but now things changed. A new, different perspective took place. I needed to calm her down . . . She is too frightened . . . She does not understand the reality of the floating life . . . yeah, I know how to calm her . . .

Then, with a voice full of confidence, the kind that I never expected from myself, I continued, "Debra, I was just joking. I didn't mean it, really. It was only a joke. Sorry. I was only teasing you."

A sigh of relief was heard, "Oh, thank God! I was worried for a moment that the seance had twisted your brain."

"Well," carefully responding, "you know Debra . . . I . . . didn't take the seance too seriously, so don't worry about that at all, and besides, I know it was all an illusion. The spirits don't really exist. You are subconsciously moving the cup, believing in ghosts." I assured her, using the logical explanation of Dr. Ron, the psychiatrist.

It worked like magic.

A great relief and new strength were detected in her voice, "Thanks for calling, David, it was nice hearing you again." Her voice sounded artificially sweet, probably remembering by now that she was talking to a kid, same age as her young brother. "I have a meeting soon," she added, "so I must hang up now. Feel free to visit us."

"Thank you for your time, Debra. Goodbye," I answered politely. And hung up, totally forgetting to tell her about the sweater. I then decided to return it in one of the coming days.

I stayed by the phone staring at it with complete disappointment. I was stuck now with no directions. She was the only "spiritual person" I knew, but a very limited one. My legs felt heavy. Slowly I went to sit on my bed.

Maybe I should ask our neighborhood's rabbi, Rabbi Avner, for some instructions . . . No. He won't help me . . . I concluded, remembering clearly how our Bible teacher at school had told us once that it was prohibited to communicate with the dead. So . . . visiting the other side . . . is probably considered even worse.

But why? After all, it was a great experience for me . . . There must be a way to get back there . . .

All of a sudden I jumped up. Yes, I know what to do! My heart was pumping fast. I hurried to the bathroom, then pulled back the colorful nylon shower curtain and filled the tub with tap water making sure the temperature was just right. I closed the door and quickly took off my clothes. Soon I was in the water face down. This is better than to try doing it in the swimming pool . . . If I was now in the public swimming pool, the lifeguard, Shula, and the other adults would probably prevent me from visiting the other side . . .

After a minute or so I raised my head from the water and breathed. Just couldn't do it. Something was preventing me from following my decision. Was it the memory of those painful, struggling moments while I had been out of breath, suffering until I had passed to the other side . . . ?

Something in me shouted "NO! DAVID, IT IS WRONG!

THERE ARE BETTER WAYS TO GET INTO THE OTHER SIDE!" Then, less alarming, the inner voice continued, "In due time you will learn how to do it by will. Be patient!" A goose bumps sensation went through my entire body. I was startled, looking around . . . Was it the being of light's voice? I wasn't sure. Immediately I grabbed a towel and dried myself, then quickly I put on my clothes and tied my old tennis shoes.

. . . I will find other ways. Now, back to my room . . . maybe I should just lie down on my bed and force myself to get out of my body, without the water . . . somehow it must work . . . I have to try it.

Throwing the pillow on the carpet, I lay down straight on my bed; this time face up. Then I stared at the ceiling as a target and tried with all of my heart to be there with the real I. Yes, I was extremely focused and put all my mental powers into it. My head felt like it was going to explode, but nothing happened. I was still in my body. I raised my head so as to push myself ahead, but it didn't help. Pushing my shoulders, hands and legs were not that helpful either. My frustration was immense. No. I didn't give up. Still in the old tennis shoes, I found myself jumping up and down on the bed, hoping that it would ease my exit.

I won't give up! No one can stop me! Not even the being of light! I will get back to the floating world one way or another. I'm going to make it! I shouted while jumping.

Unfortunately, after about an hour of jumping on the bed nothing happened. By now it had become an obsession. I wanted to get there very badly, but didn't have the slightest idea how to do it. The room was hot and humid. Being completely tired, sweating and hot, I collapsed on my stomach, hardly breathing. My heart, head and actually my entire body was still pounding rapidly. I was about to cry from frustration now. Who can help me . . . ?

Suddenly I heard the front door open. My mother entered the house. "David, are you home?"

"Yes, Mom," I responded weakly.

She hurried into my room, seeing me lying on the bed fully dressed and with a reddish, sweating face.

"Are you sick?" She looked at me in panic and immediately put her hand on my forehead. "You must have a very high fever! Get ready. We are going to see the doctor," she added, then left the room without listening to my response.

In a moment, I heard her dialing from the hallway. "May I speak to Solomon?" My mother was asking for my father. With hysterical voice she continued, "Listen! We are too busy with our work and don't spend enough time with David. It is our fault. You know he almost died yesterday. Now he is sick."

"NO! Mom! You are wrong! I feel OK. I just wanted to experience something," I shouted. But she continued ignoring my protest and then hung up.

"David, you come with me to the doctor right now." She was determined.

I knew from the past, once she decided that I needed to be seen by a doctor, even my father couldn't stop her, so there was no point in arguing. "OK," I said reluctantly, "if that's what you want."

Within a few minutes we were in the car on the way to the family doctor whom I had known all of my life. His name was Dr. Ari, a nice old man, always smiling, even when I had been in bad shape a couple of times in the past. Unlike my mother who turned hysterical each time I had a fever or any minor problem, he always seemed to be relaxed and took things easily.

We arrived at the doctor's office shortly.

"Wait here for a moment," my mother said when it was our turn to go in. She then entered Dr. Ari's room and closed the door after her.

Sitting there in the waiting-room wasn't the proper way to spend a summer vacation. Really I didn't need all this. Within a few seconds the doctor opened the door and invited me in.

"Hi, David! Good to see you again!" He grinned, looking at me through his eyeglasses.

I smiled back at him.

After a brief checking of my temperature and listening to my lungs, he then looked at my mother and announced, "Your son is perfectly healthy. There is nothing to worry about," he reassured her.

"I told her so," I protested "but she wouldn't believe me."

"You know, doctor, I bring him to see you only in serious cases." She lowered her eyes apologizing.

Unfortunately for me, she used to take me to the doctor with the first sign of fever or even when I was just tired or angry.

"Yes of course, I've known you for years. You bring him only when there is a real problem. But you know, your son is growing now, and very soon we shall see him developing into manhood. Let me talk to him privately for a while," Dr. Ari suggested to her.

"Sure," she nodded staring directly into his eyes with an understanding look, then left the room quietly.

"So what really happened, David? Would you like to talk to me about that?" he asked with a reassuring smile.

"Nothing really happened," I replied.

"David, your mother mentioned that she found you on your bed when she came home this afternoon. I have also heard about yesterday's incident, but you are not sick today. I know you are an active boy who doesn't like to take a nap during the day. On the other hand, you've already had your thirteenth birthday. You are growing and probably have different needs now. It's normal," he lowered his voice and then continued, "Were you doing anything in particular while lying on your bed, David?" He was trying to sound real caring.

Oh no, Dr. Ari has no idea what I was really doing . . . For sure he is convinced that I was playing with myself, discovering the secrets of sexual pleasure . . .

I looked at him but didn't say a word for a long moment. No, I can't tell him the truth . . . He won't understand. But maybe he will. After all he has always told me that I can tell him any secret and he would keep it confidential from my parents. I know he is an honest guy. So far he has respected all of my secrets. Maybe I can tell him. At least I can try . . . He is smart and knows a lot about life . . . He must know how to get to the floating side of life . I really hoped so.

"Are you with me, David?" Dr. Ari interrupted my thoughts.

"I'm sorry doctor." I then took a deep breath and without thinking twice said, "Dr. Ari, if I tell you something, do you promise to help me and keep it confidential?"

"Oh yes, sure. You can count on me. You know that, don't you? Did I ever betray your secrets?"

"No, Dr. Ari, but this time it is different. It is important and I don't want my parents to know about it." I was honest with him.

He looked at me with a very understanding expression on his face, I felt he really cared now. "Sure, David, I'm listening." He leaned his head toward me. His face was serious.

But as soon as I was about to express my recent wish, an inner voice, deep inside me said that there was no point in telling him the truth. But feeling Dr. Ari's understanding and care, I decided to ignore it and just give it a try.

"Dr. Ari . . . I . . . want to get back . . . to the other side, you know, the floating side."

Dr. Ari looked at me over the top of his round eyeglasses. He grew pensive, somehow worried.

"What do you mean by that, David?" he asked after a long moment.

I was silent.

"Did the drowning in the pool make you fearful or sad?"

I decided not to tell him about the time I was floating above my body nor about the huge being of light who had talked to me there. If I would, Dr. Ari might recommend to my parents not to allow me to visit the swimming pool again . . .

I assumed that it was much safer to tell him about the seance.

He looked terrified but listened very carefully, constantly nodding his head, and rubbing his chin with his right hand.

"I see, David," he murmured after I finished. "Don't you ever believe in those kinds of games! Spirits exist only in children's fairy tales or in horror stories. You are old enough to dismiss it as an illusion. Don't you ever believe in such nonsense like a seance board. Children of your age are not interested in all of these imaginary stories, unless . . . something else is happening. Is anything bothering you?" he then asked.

"Well no, not really . . . I was just curious about these phenomena. I think they are real."

Dr. Ari removed his eyeglass, cleaned them with a piece of white cloth, then put them back on. Next, he looked straight into my eyes. "David, why don't you talk about it with my friend Dr. Andrea. She is a child psychologist and knows more than I about these things."

"Does she?"

"Yes, David, besides being a very interesting person, she is the best in her profession. She knows a lot about life and how people feel and think."

The appointment was scheduled. A new hope for me. Will Dr. Andrea be the source of knowledge . . . ? I was anticipating my meeting with her.

It had been a week by now that I wasn't allowed to visit the swimming pool. In a way, I had almost forgotten about the swimming equipment and my bicycle. They will wait . . .

My mother parked the car in front of a white house with a

brown roof. "That must be Dr. Andrea's house." She was excited.

The entrance to the house was loaded with various plants, standing on both sides of the path like two lines of soldiers, leading to a brown double door.

"It will be a waste of time. She won't help you, David . . . " The inner voice, deep inside me was clear about it. But there was something else there, a strange feeling which grew with every step I made toward the house.

"She has many roses," my mother remarked, observing the front yard as she rang the bell.

A small woman with a pale, narrow face and long dark hair opened the door, "You must be Bertha." She shook my mother's hand. And you are David." She looked at me with a tiny smile. "I'm Dr. Andrea," continued the lady in a cream blouse and long black skirt. "Please come in."

She led us through a wide corridor. On the left side there was a small room with a few chairs. In the middle stood a small, low table full of newspapers and magazines. That must be the waiting room . . . I assumed while continuing to walk after Dr. Andrea. She led us to a white door on the right side of the corridor.

"This is my office." She opened the door and then turned the light on. "David, you can have a seat on the sofa. I want to talk with your mother for a moment."

She left me there and closed the door. The room was long and narrow, well-furnished in all shades of blue. A thick, blue, rectangular carpet stretched over the white tile floor, a light blue sofa was placed against the left wall and a matching minisofa was standing next to it. There were one wooden rocking chair and a small lamp stand. One small desk stood in the corner of the room next to the dark blue drape which stretched from side to side. I sat on the rocking chair and rocked myself. Finally it was boring. So I decided to go and see what's behind the drape. I peeked through . . . There, in front of my eyes, I saw a fully equipped backyard—a slide, carousel, monkey bars and swing sets, all ready to play with. It was better than any of the public parks I knew. Her children must be very happy . . .

A goose bumps sensation immediately filled my body as I thought this. I felt strange again . . . no, there is no child playing here . . . he is dead . . . yes . . . her only child is dead . . . but his soul is here . . .

"David!" Dr. Andrea called my name with a sharp tone of voice. I jumped.

"You can have a seat on the sofa. Let's start right now," she added and closed the door.

I still felt strange but did as she said.

"Now, David, tell me what is bothering you? You can trust me." She forced a smile onto her face.

After a long pause without any answer from me, she continued, "I understood from Dr. Ari that you have a secret wish to visit the other side of life. Do you wish to die?" she asked me straightforwardly, waiting for my response.

"Oh no," I answered quickly, feeling like defending myself, "I only want to visit there for a short time and then come back. Dr. Ari said that you know about these things and can help me with that." I was trying to present it as clearly as I could, although I had already known the result.

"I understand . . ." Dr. Andrea narrowed her eyes and nodded slowly. But I could see that she didn't. She didn't have the slightest idea of what she was talking about.

"Can you tell me more about this wish of yours?"

I was silent.

"Is anything bothering you so much that you attempted to commit suicide in the swimming pool last week?" She was almost attacking me with this accusation.

I was surprised as to what conclusions these adults could arrive without knowing the facts. I tried again to explain exactly what had happened with the diver, the bet, and about my experience on the other side of life while floating above my body, and that this was why I wanted to be back there, but I felt that my story only alarmed Dr. Andrea. Dr. Ari was wrong about her . . . Not only doesn't she believe me but now she thinks that I'm totally crazy . . .

"You know, David . . ." she cleared her throat, "what you just described shows me that you have strong willpower and know what you want. But you need to understand that people fantasize when they are in such traumatic situations and, after it, they simply believe their own fantasies. What you described as a floating experience was only a kind of imagination story which was created by your mind. It was not the reality."

"But, I knew it was for real," I insisted.

"Yes I understand. But, David, you are a big boy now, almost a man. Don't let these fantasies control your mind. You are the one who can decide and stop them. You are a smart boy and I know you can do it."

She is totally blind to the other reality . . . Another ignorant adult, I concluded, while looking at the blue drape. The same strange sensation filled me again now. Someone else is present in the room . . .

I kept hearing Dr. Andrea's voice in the background, but didn't really listen. For a moment I thought I saw her dead kid standing by the drape, but when I looked carefully no one was there. I turned my head slowly toward Dr. Andrea. She was still talking.

"Do you understand, David?" I finally heard her asking me.

"Yes," I answered, without even knowing to what I was replying.

"Everything was in your mind, David. Nothing was for real," she continued with assurance.

"But—" I started explaining to her again.

"David, no buts, these people who claim they have such experiences or can see such things are considered lunatics, and I know you are a smart boy who just went through a traumatic experience. You will overcome it within a few sessions." She sounded determined.

I looked at the blue drape once more. That strange sensation filled me again. Then focusing into Dr. Andrea's blue gray eyes, deep sadness went through my whole body. It became more intense the longer I looked at her. Somehow I felt I knew a lot about the small lady who sat in front of me. I could sense her fears . . . frustration . . . deep grieving cry in her heart . . . a clear loss of a dear one in her life—her son, Jonathan.

The boy was staring at me, appearing and disappearing in the room.

I will convince Dr. Andrea that she is wrong. Then maybe she will help me . . . I have to try it . . . I've got nothing to lose. She might have some way to get into the other side . . . Dr. Ari told me so . . .

"If there are not such things, as you said, and if it is only in my mind, then how come your son, Jonathan, is floating here right now?" I heard myself saying, and kept observing her son, a little boy, about six, who had suddenly reappeared so vividly near the drape.

Dr. Andrea looked at me totally shocked. She then covered her face and began crying hysterically.

"I didn't really mean to hurt your feelings," I apologized, but it didn't help . . . Well, I made a mistake again. Adults don't like to hear the truth about the other side . . . but why . . . ?

Within a second my mother was in the room. "What did you do to her?" Shouting at me and without waiting for my response, she rushed to Dr. Andrea. The small lady continued to cry, ignoring my mother.

"Tell me what happened, David!" She demanded, turning her face toward me.

I pointed toward the boy, who was by now above Dr. Andrea's head "She is crying over her dead son," I tried to explain it logically.

"Oh my God! Did she get the news now?" My mother looked horrified.

I didn't know what to say. The vision of the child in the room was something I never had experienced before. It reminded me of observing the people who had floated next to me while I had been out of my body in the swimming pool incident. Soon I realized that although the little, cute boy with the big blue eyes looked so vivid to me, Dr. Andrea and my mother couldn't see him at all.

They probably don't believe me as well . . . maybe I offended Dr. Andrea . . . Maybe talking about spirits is really offensive . . .

I got up off the sofa, observing the two hysterical ladies. I must do something . . . I can calm them . . . yeah . . . exactly like I did with Debra . . . using Dr. Ron's explanations . . .

"You know Dr. Andrea—"

None of them listened to me. My mother was supporting Dr. Andrea's head, crying loudly together with her. The boy moved toward the blue drape and observed the scene from a distance. He had no expression on his face, as if he already had given up talking to his mother.

"Excuse me," I raised my voice, feeling now as if I had to be in charge of the situation.

They both stopped crying and stared at me.

"You know Dr. Andrea, I was just joking. There was no one floating in the room. I just knew what had happened with your son, and I used this information to convince you about the other side. It was only a joke. I'm sorry. I didn't mean to offend you."

Dr. Andrea wiped her tears and released a sigh. The look on my mother's face told me I was in real trouble. Maybe it was wrong, but that was the only way I knew would calm Dr. Andrea. The crying stopped and a hateful look on the doctor's face replaced it.

"I'm so sorry about my son's behavior. I should have stayed

together with you during the session. Please forgive us. He is a good boy but sometimes he is unpredictable," my mother murmured and continued with endless apologies, giving me a hard look, which meant business. "I will deal with you at home, David," she finally said to me.

I was wondering what would happen next. All I wanted is to have some nice adventures in the other side and needed the instruction to reach there. But it seemed to me that every time I had raised the subject, or just had mentioned the spiritual world, I had been in trouble. I didn't believe anymore that the adults would help me. No, I will never tell adults about it, never, ever, I decided. By now, my wish to visit the other side got stronger, leaving me terribly frustrated.

"...his name is Dr. Nahmovich. You can tell him that I referred your son to him," I heard Dr. Andrea telling my mother as she handed to her a small piece of paper with a telephone number on it.

I understood clearly: that lady didn't want me in her office anymore.

"I won't go to any therapist," I insisted as we got home.

"Yes, you will," my mother and father said together.

"No, I won't. I feel perfectly OK. I don't need others to tell me what to think."

"David, we insist in this issue because we care about you. We love you, David! After all you had gone through a traumatic experience in which you almost died. You must get some help so that the trauma will not influence you later." My father tried to reason with me.

"Dad I'm all right. I really don't need any help. It wasn't a trauma for me at all." I insisted.

"David, from the short time I spend with you every evening, I can tell that something in you has changed since the incident. For example, you don't talk to us as much as before, you are not excited to play Chess with me anymore, and you spend hours lying down on your bed. We really think it is for your own good to go for a few sessions," my father added.

"Dad, please. I will not go. I just don't need it. They can't help me, because I don't need their kind of help!"

"Fine, David!" My mother interfered. "I'm going to call your uncle, Abraham, right now. You will not be permitted into the swimming pool anymore until you agree to visit the therapist."

Two days of no swimming pool after that argument, I was at Dr. Nahmovich's office. That time, I was completely ready for the child psychotherapist. My speech was prepared in advance. I explained to him that the whole story about leaving my body in the swimming pool had been just for the fun of it. He also got a perfect scientific explanation about the communication through the seance board. After all, he was an adult. And I knew exactly what he would love to hear from me.

Dr. Nahmovich had a big laugh with me when I described to him what had happened at Dr. Andrea's office. He gave me a moral lecture and said that I shouldn't trick adults in the future to which, of course, I agreed. He liked me.

"Your son is perfectly OK," Dr. Nahmovich assured my parents after three visits of pleasant conversation that week. Then I was free again.

Within two weeks from the drowning experience I was back in the swimming pool. My mother dropped me there on the way to her work.

"Stay safe, David," she begged. "And don't dive anymore! Promise?"

"Yes," I waved to her as I walked toward the big gate.

"David!" the receptionist welcomed me, "Good to see you again!"

"Thank you," smiling at her, I hurried to check my bike which was still there at the same corner where I had tied it. I rubbed my hand over the leather seat, feeling that actually I had missed my bike.

Soon I saw the blue water of the pool. The morning felt a little cool. Looking around, I was disappointed. Natasha wasn't there. But maybe it's too early . . . she may come later on . . . if not today, maybe tomorrow . . .

Entering the water was great. I took a deep breath smelling the freshness all around me. Some new and some familiar faces were there. No one seemed to remember the incident which had happened two weeks earlier. Shula, the lifeguard, was off duty that day. Another lifeguard whom I didn't know sat there in her place. He was busy chewing something. His eyes were hidden behind dark sunglasses. He looked as if he didn't care about anything around him.

I swam to the other side of the pool and then took a deep breath and returned, swimming back under the water. Some recollections of the bet flashed through my mind, but I felt just great. From time to time I glanced at the entrance to check who was coming in.

For the whole morning I just hoped to see Natasha again. I vividly remembered her face looking at me while my body had been lying down there. I recalled the tears in her eyes. She probably thought I was dead. If I only knew where she lives . . .

Strong splashes of water suddenly covered my head. Two boys of my age swam by. "Hi," I invited them to compete with me.

Soon we were swimming like crazy, changing swimming styles every few minutes. Occasionally I disappeared under the water and then reappeared way ahead, waving to them with a big smile.

"You are very fast," the boy with the round face told me, breathing heavily.

"Wow, how do you do that?" the other one with the freckles on his face asked.

"Practice! Practice is the only secret, guys!" I laughed with them and then disappeared under the water again, swimming to the other side of the pool.

Soon they were after me and the wild games continued all morning.

The day warmed up. I looked at the big wall clock next to the dressing room. It was almost 1:00 p.m. She must be nearby . . . I strongly felt her presence. I looked around but Natasha wasn't there. All of a sudden, I felt a warm, soft hand on my right shoulder.

"Natasha" I shouted, without even looking, then turned around and there she was, just in front of me. We hugged each other, holding tight for a long moment, not saying a word. My heart was pounding fast.

Suddenly it felt strange. I could hear thoughts—not mine, but Natasha's. It was so clear as if someone were actually telling me how she had been since we had last seen each other.

"Natasha," I looked directly into her beautiful eyes, "I know you blamed yourself and your mom for my drowning, and didn't want to talk to anyone until a week ago when you found out I was saved. I appreciate that. I'm sorry that you missed me for that long period."

Natasha was shocked, "Did my mom talk to you?"

"No," I replied, realizing that it was a mistake. I wasn't supposed to know that much.

"So how do you know?" she asked me.

"Just guessing, because of the way you are hugging me."

She gave me a pensive look and stayed silent for a moment. "I'm so happy to see you again. I was crying for a week. The thought that you were dead just didn't leave me. I knew that it would never have happened if we had played longer in the water."

"Last week my mom insisted that I should come with her

to swim here, and then we found out that you had been rescued. Since then I wanted to come here every day in the hope that you would show up. I wish I had known it earlier, but my mother and Rebecca's mother just grabbed me when I stood there crying, watching how the lifeguard and another person were trying to save your life." Natasha released a sigh.

"I missed you, Natasha. I always wished I had asked for your address or telephone number, or at least given you mine."

"Will you remember them if I tell you right now?" She looked at me with anticipation.

"I think so."

She then gave me her address and telephone number.

"Easy!" I smiled and repeated the details to her.

While talking to Natasha, I could sense that, somewhere from the coffee shop area, her mother was staring at us totally unhappy, but not daring to interrupt. Looking toward that direction only confirmed that sensation. I can ignore her mother for now . . . She will not bother us this time . . .

We swam together to a quiet corner of the pool to avoid being in direct eye contact with Natasha's mother. Holding hands under the water we continued to talk, looking into each other's eyes as we did. My heart filled with a warm sensation that kept spreading throughout my entire body. It was a kind of completely joyful feeling, as if the whole world stopped moving around. The noisy pool became quiet, like nothing else existed in the world, only she and I. Our lips found each others . . . we let go, kissing each other for the first time. It was a great moment in my life. She is the one with whom I can share myself . . . I wanted to be with her forever. Yeah . . . I can share my love and secrets with her . . .

"Natasha," I said to her after the magical moment was over, "I want to tell you something, but please keep it secret."

Natasha looked at me surprised, "OK." She took a deep breath.

I then started to tell her everything that had happened to

me since the bet, how I struggled in the water to finish and to reach the other side of the pool, and how I found myself leaving the body through a narrow pipe, eventually watching the whole rescue scene while I was floating in the sky.

"So you saw me, too!" She was excited.

"Yes, Natasha, I followed you. I saw exactly how they grabbed you from each side and how the three of you made your way through the crowd who encircled my body."

". . . Right!" she shouted, folding her arms.

"Rebecca was waiting there" I pointed to an area next to a tree, "and then you all went home together."

She stared down rubbing her arms. "I am cold, look at my skin," She shivered.

I hugged her. "Do you want to sit in the sun?"

"Yes, I think it is a good idea."

We left the pool and went to an isolated corner on the meadow. From there we could view the whole pool area including the coffee shop.

Natasha waved to her mother, who didn't remove her eyes from us.

"Tell me more about it" she asked as we sat on the grass.

I continued, not missing any detail. Natasha listened quietly. She was very excited.

"If you ever get out of your body again, come to visit me, OK?" she told me seriously. She understood my point that it wasn't a death wish on my part, but only a real need for more adventures and exploration of life. She could grasp it better than all those adults around me who were so blocked by their own education, or maybe fears, thus refusing to see reality.

The time with Natasha went by quickly. It started to be late. Her mother slowly walked toward us. This time she acknowledged me by nodding her head.

"It's time to go home, Natasha." She looked at her daughter, ignoring me now.

Natasha and I stood up on the soft meadow and gave each other a quick hug. "Keep in touch," she whispered.

"I will," I promised, missing her already.

The next morning I couldn't wait to meet Natasha. As soon as my parents left, I picked up the phone and dialed the number I had learned by heart.

"Do you want to come over to my house? My mom went shopping. Then at about 3:45 she needs to pick up my sister from the day care. She won't be here before 4:00 in the afternoon." Natasha was enthusiastic.

An hour later we were together. This time it was different. Being at her home, with no one to supervise us, was so relaxing but, at the same time, I felt a high voltage current all over my body. I was excited and trembling. Yes. I was in love, feeling it in my heart and everywhere else in my body. The time passed so quickly that when we heard the door bell ringing and her mother came in, it was a very unpleasant surprise for all of us. If Natasha's mother could, I guess, she would throw me out the window, but she tried to stay cool. She quickly put Natasha's little sister in a high chair facing the kitchen, and placed a bottle in her hands. Then she looked at me and commented cynically, "I see, David, that you found us very quickly. Don't you have some homework to do?"

"No, ma'am," I responded quietly. "It is the summer vacation, you know."

"Yes, yes, I know. But Natasha has her ballet class and she takes piano lessons as well. She needs to practice. I guess you don't have anything like that, otherwise you wouldn't be in that swimming pool all day," she added in a sarcastic voice and looked at Natasha.

"Yes, you are right. I don't have classes in the summer. My parents believe in relaxation and time for vacations as well.

Everything in life should be balanced," I answered. Then I politely apologized and left for my home.

It was nearly 5:00 p.m. when I arrived home only to hear that Natasha's mother already had called my mother, asking her to forbid me to meet her daughter ever again, and complaining that I was a bad influence on her daughter.

"No way. No one will stop me from seeing her," I exclaimed swiftly, and decided to keep our meetings in secret.

We met a few times outside her house and spent wonderful times in nature, in the isolated fields. Unfortunately for us, a few weeks later Natasha and her parents went on vacation out of the country and then never returned to our city. Before she left, we had exchanged photos. Somehow I had felt that I would not see her for a long time. I didn't know if her parents had acted that way in order to separate us, or if it had been planned. The results were the same—I couldn't see her anymore. It was painful to love someone and not be able to see that person. How unfair life is . . . yeah . . . one day I will see her again . . . I know it . . . but when?

September arrived and soon I was back in school. During that year I constantly tried to visit the other side of life, but without any success. Something was missing in my efforts, but I never gave up. At least once per day I tried to get out of my body, while keeping it totally secret from everyone. Each night, just before I fell asleep, I used to whisper to the being of light, asking him to help me and show me the way to get out of my body again or, at least, be in touch as he had promised. But no matter what I did, I couldn't get out. However, something was changing constantly in me during those months. Occasionally, I could feel or hear others' thoughts and knew specific things about their lives. I learned to hide it from others, so as not to embarrass anyone. My vision reached a different dimension.

Sitting in back of the classroom, at one of the desks in the last row, I remember how, one afternoon, about forty heads including that of the teacher glowed with various shades of white, yellow and a variety of other changing colors. Then how actually everything was glowing, even the desks and the chairs, but there was a difference. The furniture's glow was like a static white frame, somehow different from the vivid glow of my classmates and teacher.

I then realized that whenever I wanted, I could switch from regular vision to seeing these energies around everything. Soon I found out that when I did it, I could occasionally see other types of energies, other than the ones around objects or people. These energies were usually formless, but sometimes they were actually vivid floating people who were everywhere. Remembering Jonathan, Dr. Andrea's son, I wondered if he showed up only at her house or was floating outside as well. I didn't try to communicate with these floating spirits, simply because I didn't think they wanted to talk with me. They were just observing me silently with no attempt to talk with me at all.

The last year of grammar school flew by quickly. At the second part of that period, it was time for me to decide which high school to attend. A marine boarding school was a natural choice for me. I loved the water, was a good athlete and besides, I couldn't travel into the other side, so at least I could join the merchant marine as a sea officer and . . . see the world. There was only one problem—my grades at grammar school were very bad, which made it very doubtful that I would ever be admitted to the marine boarding school.

Somehow they were willing to interview me and let me participate in the series of tests which were part of the prerequisites for admission into the marine boarding school.

A month later I was invited for another interview. This

time with the school's vice-principal. My father and I woke up early in the morning and drove all the way along the Mediterranean Sea. We arrived there just on time and signed for the interview. Within fifteen minutes I was in.

"Have a seat, David." The vice-principal grinned.

I sat quietly.

"I reviewed your application and a copy of your grammar school's grade sheet. It seems that you don't really like to study."

I lowered my head.

"But on the other hand, David," he continued, "the score of your IQ test is extremely high. In fact, one of the highest scores ever achieved at this school."

I looked into his eyes, knowing deep inside that this was going to be my high school.

"Yes, David, it is unusual, but this shows me that you have the capability to be a great student if you decide to sit and learn. The committee discussed your case and we are willing to let you attend this school—but only if you promise to invest in yourself. Now, it is really up to you," he added and then paused for a moment. "Do you think you can invest in yourself?" He looked directly into my eyes.

At that moment I knew he was right. I never had made any efforts at grammar school. Somehow I just didn't care. I won the city Chess contest for youth and was good in art. I did read a lot of books from the library—instead of doing homework—and played hours on the streets. I really liked to do what I liked to do, and nothing else. But, this time it was different . . . It was serious . . . I wanted to be admitted into this marine boarding school very badly and the vice-principal's words touched me. He was willing to trust me. Yes, I decided that I am going to make the effort.

"I promise I'll do my best to be a good student in your school, Sir." I stared at him, meaning every word I said.

"Very good, David." He smiled and then took a deep

breath. "I'll be here. And if you have any problems, I want you to feel free to tell me. We will try to help you, although I believe you will be fine."

He then got up from his chair and followed me to the door. "By the way, David, the physical fitness and the swimming test reports also showed outstanding results." He tapped on my shoulder, then looked at my father who was waiting outside and shook his hand with a smile.

A few minutes after the meeting we were on our way home. We traveled along the highway which bordered the coast. The blue sea looked clear, quiet and inviting. I'm going to spend a great deal of my life there . . . My heart was pounding rapidly with joy.

The summer vacation went by quickly. I missed Natasha. I hadn't seen her for almost a year now. Nevertheless there were always fun things to do in the pool, so I enjoyed that summer and felt stronger. Everyone knew I was accepted at the marine boarding school and wished me luck.

The big day arrived and I was again with my father on our way to the marine boarding school. He was silent all the way there. I sensed his pain. Dad is going to miss me . . . also Mom, she has been crying all night.

My father parked the car in front of the main building of the school. Many boys of my age and older ones were there in the open yard. They all wore gray uniforms, like miniature soldiers. My father and I stood there next to the car for a long moment.

"I'll be fine, Dad." I assured him.

"Yes, I know, son." He smiled at me with sadness in his eyes.

"I love you, Dad." I gave him a hug and then quickly wiped

the small tears that filled the corners of my eyes.

"Let me help you to your room, David." He was about to lift my heavy suitcase.

"I'm OK. I'm strong enough to carry everything by my-self," I added and hugged him again. Then I took the heavy suitcase and hung the bag over my shoulder, and marched to-ward the main building, where a big sign pointed to "FIRST YEAR ADMISSION."

Looking back, I saw that he was still standing there by the car.

"We'll see you in a few weeks, kiddo." My father shouted, waving to me. I waved back with my free hand. Then with a great excitement I entered the huge building. I didn't know what to expect.

"This is your room." The housemother showed me in. "You are going to share it with three more boys. You can put your stuff over there." She pointed to a wooden cabinet next to one of the beds on the right side of the room.

I nodded, observing the room.

"Hurry up! Soon you will have your first morning parade," she told me with a smile.

My first day at the marine boarding school began, and so did my new approach as a student. I took things seriously from the start, kept all the rules, was punctual, and did all my home-work. Contrary to grammar school, I soon found myself one of the best students in my class. The vice-principal was right. I thanked him inside my heart, feeling that his words and trust in me had really awakened me to study seriously. Then I also remembered how my father used to tell my mother not to worry about my grades, "He can learn anything he wants, but it is up to him," he always had been confident about it. Now I realized that he was right as well.

The schedule was tight with almost no free time except for

a few hours at night after we were done with homework. We had a tough military discipline with a full day's activity, starting early in the morning until late in the evening, with a few breaks for meals in between. The first part of the day usually was dedicated to the high school curriculum, then, from 3:00 in the afternoon until around 7:00, to professional marine activities. These included sailing, carpentry, electricity lab and, of course, swimming and physical endurance.

The sea was great. We learned how to operate rowing boats. First we had to practice how to row in a team while the boats were tied with ropes to the pier. We had to repeat the practice time and time again.

The military discipline was much tougher than the curriculum discipline I had had during grammar school. Here they had the point system for every single, minor wrong thing you did, even if you didn't really mean it. Anyone who reached a hundred points was suspended for good. Three kids were thrown out of school during the first two months. Yeah, it was different from anything I previously had known, but even so, I liked it and sensed that I was in the right atmosphere for me, with its high activity and routines. I was a quiet person usually, but felt the love of my classmates, instructors and teachers around me.

The months passed by quickly and winter arrived. Every night I continued to ask the being of light to help, so I could go out of my body, but he didn't show up. It became like a prayer, unfortunately with no results. Nevertheless, I continued asking.

Then, one cold evening in December, I felt extremely tired. It was after a regular day full of school studies, physical training and, of course, completion of the endless homework for the next day.

"We are going to play table tennis, are you coming, David?" my roommates asked on their way out to the school club.

"No, I'll stay here this evening."

"You are not sick or something," one of them asked.

"No, just a little tired." I had planned to rest for awhile and then maybe read an adventure book.

"See you later, buddy." They left the room, closing the door after themselves.

I turned off the lights and lay down on my back with my clothes on. I was tired and the bed felt so good. The room was dark and quiet. I was just about to close my eyes and take a nap. All of a sudden, in the darkness, I noticed that the room was changing in colors as if it became full of lights, yet no one was there to turn on the lights, and besides, these were totally different lights. I kept lying down with my eyes wide opened, witnessing the strange phenomenon. A soft, bright light gradually filled the room now. The center of that light grew denser as if a heavy cloud was molded in it. Becoming completely alarmed, I kept following everything. Soon I felt like I was tightly glued into my bed, totally paralyzed. My heart was pumping fast as I held my breath. Suddenly I saw him. Yes, that was the spirit, the being of light, who had sent me back into my body that day in the swimming pool. His head touched the ceiling. He wasn't as tall as he appeared to be out there. He also looked a little different, but no doubt, it was he. Gradually I calmed down. I wasn't alarmed or afraid anymore. My whole being filled with endless joy.

"Did you come to take me with you?" I asked him, hoping . . .

"NO, David, it is not yet your time. You have a lot of work to do here. Your destiny demands much more." I heard his voice as if it were coming from inside my head, but I knew it wasn't me. It was a completely different voice from my inner voice or thoughts.

"I came here to fulfill your dream. It is time for you to

learn how to get out of your body, in a simple way, using your own will. Yes David, your prayers do manifest themselves. I'm going to instruct you how to leave your body, as you so much requested after the incident in the swimming pool."

"OK, but, I'm too tired" I added spontaneously, hoping it was still OK.

The angel only smiled. I could hardly see the shape of his face, yet it was clear to me that he was smiling.

"Let's see about that," he responded in a loving voice.

He was illuminating with more intensity now which lit up the room much more. Soon I felt endless, powerful, vibrating, warm light passing through my body. I just didn't move myself, letting it fill my whole being. In a few seconds, I became totally alert as if I had drunk tons of coffee from my father's forbidden, strong, Turkish coffee. I was trembling involuntarily, yet it wasn't scary. I felt completely secure, as if I were totally protected in a blanket of love and warmth.

"David," the angel then smiled, "you have a lot to experience and learn but soon you will be ready.

"Now relax and count backward from ten to one . . . close your eyes. You still can see me this way. I will be with you all the way out," he assured me.

I started counting down, hearing him inside my head. A peaceful relaxation took place. I couldn't feel the bed anymore.

"Continue to relax, David," the angel told me with loving, radiating voice. "Put all of yourself in the upper part of your head. Now, be one with the heartbeat as if you are the heart and nothing else. Once you feel you are the heart, shift your attention to your stomach . . . be the stomach . . . then shift your attention to your feet . . . be there. In every part or organ of your body that you put your attention on, be that part and nothing else. Then move to the other parts. From the feet move your attention to the legs, then to the pelvic area, continue up to the stomach again, to the heart again, to the throat, and then to the center between the eyes. Next, move into the top of the head . . . stay there for a few minutes . . . try to feel vibrations in your head . . . "

He continued to instruct me, step by step. His voice was calm and reassuring. Following his instructions, I was in a state of complete relaxation and at the same time totally energetic, awake and refreshed. Soon I started to feel my real self again.

"What you feel now, David, is your ageless soul. Respect it. Love it. Remember, you are not your body, but you stay in your body. Be aware of it all the way through and continue to relax . . . Now, move down with your soul and feel the chest again . . . be in your heart . . . yes, good. Now move up to your stomach . . . good."

Continuing to follow his instructions, I visited every part of my body, section by section, over and over again. My eyes were closed, but I kept seeing him as if I had left them wide open. Incredible, how was he doing all this? I wondered as I followed his voice.

"David, you shouldn't analyze anything now. When you do that, you activate your logical brain which will prevent you from getting out of your body."

"OK," I answered, without using my lips, a little ashamed that he could know what I was thinking.

"Now, radiate love . . . thank your body and promise your body that you're leaving it temporarily and you will be back in a short period of time . . . " the angel continued with his instruction and I kept following them one after another. Then came the moment I was waiting for. "I want you to sense the feeling in your throat now . . . This is the door for you to get out of your body, David. Yes, the best opening door for you is in your throat. Always be aware of this opening. It is your first key for getting out of your body by will. Later, you will master other ways to travel out of your body. Now give me your hand, I'm outside of you. Here, my hand is near your throat."

I saw him very close to me. His hand was glowing like a

neon light in a cloud. It wasn't solid. I then slowly sent my soul's hand through my throat. All of a sudden, I felt his powerful, yet soft, hand pulling me very strongly out of my body. Wow! I was out of my body again!

It all happened rapidly. It felt different from the first time there in the pool. Now I was relaxed, more in control, totally awake, anticipating the exit. The passage seemed shorter with a shining light at its end. Moving through that tube, I felt that I was actually just passing through my own throat, outside into the room. In that split second, I wondered if this was the long, dark pipe or tunnel which I had passed through the first time. My feelings were answering a clear, positive yes. I was happy. I'm free . . . I'm back home . . .

Yes, the out-of-body state was suddenly more natural and familiar to me than being inside of my body. The sensation of freedom was enormous. The angel wasn't holding my hand anymore and, by now, I was observing my surroundings, floating above my body, which was lying down, face up.

Looking through the window, I was amazed. It had been dark outside when my friends left for the club, but now at about 8:30 p.m., it seemed as if the whole world were actually illuminated. A soft, bright, white light, whose source I didn't know, was shining everywhere inside and outside the room. I looked at the angel. He smiled at me with reassurance and love. I felt like a baby who was exploring his new world. Within a few more seconds I got used to my new, old situation and felt the satisfaction and happiness which had been filling my soul when I first left my body. The angel looked at me with love.

"I have to leave you now, David," he suddenly said to me, as endless love and caring were radiated from his voice.

"Why can't you stay with me?" I felt as if I were missing him already.

"It is time for your self-training, David. From now on, you should start the training by yourself in this level of existence. When you are ready, I will be with you again. Now that you know how to get out of your body, the rest is practice. Yes, David, practice your new dimension every day until you are ready to advance further. Remember to practice exactly as you did today, then explore your world and you will be fine."

With these words inside of my soul's head, he disappeared, leaving me floating in the room. Looking down at my body, I noticed myself being in a floating state, very close to the ceiling. Excitement filled my entire being. I was free . . .

Then, after a while, I wanted to move around the room, but I didn't know how, so I started with a swimming like movement. Unfortunately I remained on the same spot. Within a few moments of experimentation, I understood the principle of moving in the out-of-body state—simply by the use of my will. If you want to be at a specific point, all you have to do is exercise your will; wish to be there and instantly you are there, as simple as that. So, I floated toward the door and tried to open it with my soul's hand, but soon realized that it was impossible. Next time I will leave the door open . . .

All of a sudden I sensed that someone was walking in the corridor toward my room. What if my friends should enter the room and find my body on the bed without any movement . . . I was worried. But thinking logically I knew that they would probably assume I was still sleeping and by then I would have enough time to be back in my body. But what if they'll think I have fainted and call the class instructor . . . ? I might be removed from school . . .

Then, in a split second, I was vacuumed back toward my body, falling at a great speed, hitting my body as I entered it, without any control. It wasn't a pleasant sensation at all. It took me a few seconds to overcome that unexpected move. Then I tried to understand what had really happened to me since I had lain down to have a nap.

Was I dreaming . . . ? I pinched myself on my left arm, just to make sure that I wasn't. I probably pinched too hard. It was painful and left me totally awake, very much refreshed, as if I had slept the whole evening. My reflecting watch showed that only forty-two minutes had passed by. Maybe I was asleep after all. Maybe this event was just another dream . . . Is it possible that the angel would help me . . . ? Wasn't he the one who had pushed me back into my body in the first place? Why then would he want to help me this time . . . ? What is the difference . . . ? I just couldn't tell.

While lying in bed, thinking, I heard my friends' footsteps, closer now, in the corridor.

"Shhh, let's be quiet, David is asleep," Joe was whispering to the other two. I didn't move.

Yeah, I felt they were coming back to the room . . . while I was out of my body . . . so maybe it was a real experience after all . . .

Just before the lights-out time announcement was heard, I quickly got out of my bed and went to take a shower. Walking back to my room, the boarding school was dark and quiet. I slowly lay down on my bed, but trying to solve the mystery, I couldn't fall asleep. No clear solution crossed my mind. Finally, late at night, I decided that the real proof would be to try getting out of my body by will, according to the angel's instructions. I turned my head and looked carefully toward my roommates. They were sound asleep.

I then took a deep breath and decided to begin counting backward. But what if they will notice . . . ? I realized that I couldn't do it in their presence.

Eventually, I decided to wait until the next night when they would leave for the club again. I was full of excitement waiting for tomorrow. Finally I closed my eyes and fell asleep.

"It's wake-up time! Wake-up everyone!" I heard the housemother announcing to start the new day as she did routinely every morning.

I jumped from my bed and went to the dormitory shower room at the end of the corridor. Then I returned to the room and quickly fixed my bed. I just couldn't wait for the day to pass by.

"Good morning," I welcomed my roommates who had just gotten up from their beds.

"Good morning, David." They looked surprised.

"You did it pretty fast today," Tom, one of my roommates commented.

"Yeah, I guess so." I smiled and then tied my shoes.

The morning parade took forever. But I marched as everyone else did.

"Right! Left! Right! Left! . . . Stand in place! Relax!" the officer shouted and began the regular attendance checking.

"Sam"

"Here!"

"Toby"

"Here!"

I still have time . . . My name is among the last ones to be called . . . I looked straight ahead toward the horizon where the sky kissed the wide blue sea. Very soon I will be floating over there . . . Recalling the previous night, I imagined how free and joyful I had been . . .

A sudden push from my friend's elbow interrupted my thoughts.

"David?" I heard the officer calling my name.

"Here!" I quickly shouted, feeling embarrassed. I didn't know how many times he had called my name. I hope . . . I won't get points for that . . . I was trying to stay alert for the rest of the parade.

Eventually it was over. We all went toward the dining hall.

"Smells good!" My roommate, Joe said.

"Yeah." I continued walking quietly.

"What's the matter with you, David?" Joe asked apparently worried about me.

"I'm fine. I wonder what's for breakfast today."

"For sure the usual bread, sour cream, cheese and eggs," he replied looking at me pensively.

The tables were well-organized, full of the typical Israeli breakfast items; various kinds of cheeses, sour cream, yogurt, cereals, cucumber and tomato salad, olives, scrambled eggs, fresh baked rolls, chocolate spread, jelly, hot cocoa, tea and fresh milk.

Usually I had a good appetite in the morning, but that morning I just couldn't eat much and wished that time would pass faster.

During the class hours I hardly stayed focused. I kept thinking about the angel and memorizing the instructions for leaving my body.

"Are you OK, David?" My math teacher, Reuben, looked worried about me.

I nodded, apologizing. Then I really tried to concentrate on my study. Unfortunately, only two hours later, I suddenly heard my astronomy teacher calling my name, "David, are you there?"

"Yes," I answered, trying not to think anymore about my plan.

I was totally confused, waiting for the evening to arrive. Some of my friends sensed I was going through something, but somehow they didn't ask questions.

The evening arrived. We were all doing our homework at school, in one of the classrooms. Soon I'll stay by myself . . . but for now I have to continue with my homework . . .

Then when we reached our room an hour later, as if on purpose, my roommates didn't seem to leave for the club that evening. They stayed in the room casually chatting about girls. I was pretty quiet, didn't participate much in the conversation.

"You look strange today, David," Aaron murmured.

"Really?" I put a surprised look on my face.

"Yeah, he is right, David," Joe added, "The teachers noticed that you were daydreaming as well."

"Don't worry, I'm fine, just a little tired," I assured them, looking at my bed.

They are not leaving the room tonight . . . I guess I will have to do my out-of-body practice while they are asleep . . .

Soon it was 10:00 p.m. Outside the night was dark and cold, but it felt just right in the room.

"It's lights-out time!" The voice of the housemother was heard from the corridor as usual.

We all went to our beds. I was lying quietly on my stomach, waiting until my three roommates would fall asleep. Eventually they did one after the other. A complete silence dominated the whole dormitory where my entire class was located.

Turning on my back, face up, I fixed my blanket and placed my hands along my body, staring at the ceiling.

Next, I took a few deep breaths, exhaling the air from my lungs. Closing my eyes, I started to count down slowly from ten to one, imagining to myself that the angel was with me now. Soon I felt my whole being as a separate entity from my body. I started to move inside of my body, visiting each part, from the head . . . then to the heart . . . and then again to the head . . . Remembering the angel's instructions, I continued to visit the various parts of my body, shifting from one to another. I then tried to concentrate on my throat and decided that it was time to leave. But it didn't work. I continued being aware of the real I, visiting the various parts of my body and then acknowledged my physical body with love and respect. After about an hour of practicing, I condensed myself in the throat area. By now I was completely relaxed and ready to leave my body. Then it happened. The passage sensation through my throat was clear. It felt as if I were passing again in that long, big tube at an enormous speed. At its end was a bright light. Soon I reached that light. I was outside my body!

Great! I did it! By myself! I can really leave my body using my own will! My hopes, my dreams have become a reality.

I looked down and watched my body lying on the bed, then observed my roommates to make sure they were sound asleep.

After the initial minutes of excitement, I realized that the dark room was not dark anymore. A constant bright light filled the room from all directions, enabling me to see perfectly clearly, as if it were full daylight or even better than that. Looking toward the window, I saw that the same bright light was outside, too.

I guess this light is permanent in the floating side . . . I was trying to understand the new reality. Then, looking at my watch, which was next to my pillow, I realized it was 11:45 p.m.

By now it was time to get out of the room and to see the outside. Floating toward the door, I realized that I had just forgotten to leave it slightly opened as I had planned to do.

What shall I do now?

I had no idea and just continued to float near the door. But suddenly I just got it. Yes, simply using my own will to be there will take me there, exactly as I could move around the room . . .

To my delight, in a split second, I was floating out of the room, in the corridor, exactly where I had wanted to be.

I was excited and felt very proud of myself. The happiness which, by now, simply filled my entire soul was something I will never forget. Yes, I decided to remember these great moments forever; my first time of leaving the body by my own will is history.

Soon I was floating outside above the dormitory, closer to the roof. The scene was beautiful. Bright light filled the whole world around me, revealing an enormous life activity. It was just amazing. The sky was actually full of entities, mostly in the shape of humans, but there were also other life forms which I couldn't even recognize. I was watching them, seeing clearly in all directions. They were watching me, too, as they floated by. Then I looked down. There was our security guard. His eyes were closed. He was taking a short nap, not really knowing that someone was watching him from the sky.

Looking to my left at the street that bordered our school, I saw five young men walking there. They wore heavy raincoats, warm hats and boots, probably some night shift workers in one of the factories nearby. I then realized I just wasn't cold at all. It just felt really pleasant. A few cars crossed the highway near the school. They did it at a high speed; their engines sounded clearer than ever. Although the school was about three miles from the highway, it was quiet but with a clear and sharp sound as if I were near the engines hearing each piston in each car. Simultaneously, a soft, special, rich, music was heard in the background. It sounded familiar, peaceful . . . Yeah, I had heard that music when I was of out of my body the first time, during the pool incident.

Then all of a sudden I was alarmed. Far away from me, I noticed a huge creature. What's that . . .? I wondered with fear.

It was floating toward my direction. Soon I saw a dark, gray, ten stories high monster in the shape of a spider. It had two gigantic, penetrating, bright eyes that looked at me with a cold, cruel look, as if I were its chosen prey. No . . . can't be . . . maybe it's just a nightmare . . .

I felt alarmed as if in real danger. Not knowing what to do, I froze in the middle of the air, just above our dormitory.

The spider glided faster now.

I called for help with all my power, but none of the other floating spirits around me seemed to bother at all. I looked down toward the security guard. He was still asleep. Even if he was awake, he could not help me . . .

I was completely terrified. The monster was getting closer and closer now. Then it suddenly happened. In a split second I found myself falling with an enormous speed back into my body, feeling the big hit as I entered it. Trembling from fear I opened my eyes and after awhile sat on my bed, feeling as if my life had been saved by a miracle .

Am I safe now . . . ? I wasn't sure anymore. My heart was racing. I looked around. The room was dark. My friends were in a deep sleep.

. . . Life can be much better without these spirit monsters . . . No wonder, then, why adults refuse to participate in the other side of life, or even discuss it . After all, it is a dangerous world . . . I pulled up the blanket and covered my face. It might be safer this way . . . who knows . . .

By now, I could understand all those parents who acted to protect their kids from such monsters, teaching them to ignore the spiritual world, as if by ignoring that dimension of reality, it couldn't affect the living side of life . . . If you can't see them, they don't exist for you . . . What a funny concept, yet some-how it seems possible . . . I sure hope so . . .

"But . . . maybe the adults are just completely blind to the other side of life . . . ?" An inner voice in me protested, but I decided to ignore it, at least for now.

That night I was cold, unable to relax or sleep. Trembling for a few hours, I kept recalling everything I had seen outside. I was afraid to close my eyes, worried that the monster spider would come into my dreams, but eventually I fell into a deep, dreamless sleep.

Next morning I woke up tired. I stayed in my bed, think-ing with agony about the world that I had so much wanted to be a part of. I lost it . . . I will never go back . . . the other side of life has its own dangers . . . it is not so simple after all . . . So why then did the angel teach me to get out of my body? I won-dered. He was so full of love and warmth. No. He wouldn't let me endanger myself. But maybe he didn't care . . . ? But what actually could the spider do to me? Could he just eat my soul . . . ? Or maybe just swallow me . . . ?

In the mysterious realm of the other side, I felt that everything was possible. I didn't understand the rules of the Universe, and no one was nearby to tell me about it. Yes, I was lonely in this realm, accepting slowly the idea that it wasn't a safe or a fun dimension after all.

. . . but, maybe I can learn more about how to be safe in the other side of life . . .? Maybe there is a way . . . No. It's too dangerous a place . . . better stay in this side of life and be like all my other friends, simply forget about the floating side . . .

The next night I went to the club, had sports activities and totally ignored my training. It wasn't for me anymore, I decided. But another part of me screamed, "David, you should practice. It is for your own good!" Ignoring that inner voice, I was determined to focus on the school activities as all of the other cadets did, just to stay away from that world, at least until I could figure out how to protect myself in the other realm. But there was something in there that attracted me like a magnet with such a tremendous force that it left me helpless, wanting it and at the same time being afraid of it. I had a series of questions and problems without anyone to answer them for me. At that time I realized how little knowledge I really had of the other side.

Every night, almost like a prayer to him, I kept asking the angel to come and teach me how to protect myself in the other side, but my requests obviously were ignored. It simply didn't work. Neither the angel nor anyone else came to give me some advice on the vital protection I needed while on the other side of life. At some times I was so angry at the angel that I would scream to him in my mind, hoping he was listening to me: "If you don't come to me now, I will never get out of my body and all of your instructions will be good for nothing!" Unfortunately this approach wasn't working either. The angel simply didn't show up.

5
The Initiation

For the next few weeks, I didn't try to get out of my body, or even to participate in any training as I was instructed to do by the angel. The event of encountering what I eventually called the *evil spider*, *evil spirit*, or the *monster*, was too strong a trauma for me. Even the memory of those few seconds was chilling, freezing my entire body. The only thing which was, in my opinion, equivalent to the encounter with the monster, was the knowledge that the prehistoric man had to encounter dinosaurs face to face. Now I could understand the enormous fear that the prehistoric man probably had when meeting the giant, vicious dinosaurs. The only difference was that, in my case, I felt it was a thousand times more dangerous. There is no place to hide . . . The monster can reach you in a split second . . . I still could remember very vividly how it was gliding with enormous speed, straight toward me . . . its eyes big and wide open . . . looking directly at me. Lucky for us these kinds of monsters don't exist in the physical world . . . Yes, we are lucky to live in a physical world rather than in the dangerous, other side world, I thought.

I couldn't understand how come I had been so innocent and enthusiastic about being, or wishing to live, in the other side of life. But then something in me kept asking: How come that all the departed ones can survive those spirits . . . ? Are we the prey to those monsters after we die . . . ? But no, it is impossible. I saw the spirits of people who had died, and they still exist . . . they don't seem to be so much afraid, if at all, so what is the truth . . . ?

Many questions about the other side of life kept occupying my mind. It wasn't a logical world. It didn't make much sense to me. How come the evil spider didn't harm me . . . ? How come I could return to the room or actually to my body with no harm . . . ? That creature was so fast and big . . . if it wanted to catch or attack me, it could do it easily . . . maybe I was faster . . . I don't know . . .

But whether it made sense or didn't, just the memory of those cold, cruel eyes looking at me was more than enough to keep me away from this strange dimension of life, which I perceived by now as a dangerous place to be or even to visit. I became tense, occasionally watching the sky suspiciously, just in case that the monster would penetrate my daily physical realm. Although I considered myself as strong and fast, I wasn't very confident in myself anymore. The reality of the physical world and the other reality didn't match. My attention and concentration at school were reduced to nearly zero by now. This naturally affected my studies and it showed in the results of the various tests. From an "A" student I became a "C" and "D" student. My teachers were aware of my stress, but had no idea who or what was causing it. I couldn't talk about it, nor ask for their help. My parents were out of the picture as well. I couldn't mention such an adventure to them at all. Playing games at the school club seemed boring now, and even the food became tasteless. Yeah, I had to handle the stress by myself.

Every night, just before going to sleep, I found myself dedicating about five minutes trying to contact the angel, no matter how tired or sleepy I was. It wasn't exactly as a prayer, but as an honest request to an angel who had promised to help and whose word I had trusted. "Angel, please help me. Please talk to me again," I used to murmur quietly, but no one showed.

About three cold months passed by. I was disappointed and ready to quit calling the angel. Better just to forget him . . .

I was afraid that, for some reason, he would never come back again although I had been calling him every night. By now it was without much hope; he had abandoned or forgotten about me. But I was wrong . . .

One night, in February, when I was asleep as usual in my room at the dormitory, the angel suddenly appeared in my dream. I was excited. My whole body was shaking and goose bumps covered my entire skin. Although I was asleep, I could feel it clearly. He talked to me with love, shedding his light on me.

"David, I am waiting for you to continue with your exercises. You are safe. I know what happened to you. The encounter with the spirit was traumatic for you, but believe me, you should not fear the monster. It is an illusion. It is not a real monster, only a small spirit pretending to be big and scary.

"Remember, you are protected by me and the Divine Forces of the Universe, therefore, do not be afraid. You were supposed to practice and exercise your new awareness but, instead, you became afraid of an illusion, and you are ready to quit. David, wake up, I will help you once again to get out of your body."

"But it was a real monster. It is too dangerous. It is not for me." I explained to him in my dream.

The angel smiled at me. "Wake up, David, and be ready for your next adventure in the other realm of life".

All of a sudden I woke up, not feeling tired at all. All my senses were wide awake. I was very alert. Looking around, my other roommates seemed to be sleeping. The night was cold. Only a faint light from the moon entered the room through the shades.

For a few minutes I kept recalling the detail of the dream in my mind but, at the same time, I couldn't believe that there was anything real in that dream. Then focusing on my immediate needs, I quickly removed my blanket and went out to the restroom. It was hard to leave the warm bed. I then hurried back to my room, thinking maybe that had been the reason for me to wake up, so I quickly jumped under the blanket and was ready to sleep again. But somehow, as soon as I closed my eyes, I had a shaky feeling, now remembering the vivid dream more strongly. Was it a dream or a reality . . . ? How can I know if the angel visited me . . . ? He never had answered my calls for him even though I have called him every night . . . Was the angel playing with me? Was it a reality? How can I tell . . . ? Should I trust this dream . . . ? Well, eventually I decided to ignore it. A dream is a dream, and you cannot trust a dream . . . and as far as I remembered the explanations of my father about dreaming: "It is a simple and natural mechanism of processing or even digesting the many events in life. You cannot take a dream as reality." Yeah, If the angel wants to talk to me, fine. He has then to manifest himself and come when I am awake . . .

Looking at my watch I saw that it was 1:20 a.m. It's too late and, besides, tomorrow I have to wake up early for a special sport activity of the class . . . I'd better go to sleep now.

With that conclusion I closed my eyes and soon I was sound asleep.

But, suddenly I was dreaming again . . . An illuminated figure in the dark, was standing by my bed. "Wake up, wake up, David. Trust me, David," I soon recognized the angel's voice talking to me again—now with urgency. My whole body shook. Totally awake, I opened my eyes.

I looked at my watch. It showed 1:45 a.m.; less than half-an-hour had passed since I had first awakened. What's going on with me . . . ? Was it a dream that repeated itself just because I wanted it so much to happen . . . ? I tried another logical explanation from the many talks with my father.

But no, this time I felt it was different. The inner voice in me once again told me, " David, the angel is trying to communicate with you through the dream state. Accept it. It is what you were waiting for."

I didn't know how the angel could do it, but nevertheless it seemed natural for him to do just that. I still was a little bit shaky but, by now, my curiosity arose. I have to find out . . . I have to use determination and courage for checking the reality . . . only then will I know if it was a dream or reality . . . yeah, then I'll find out if it was a real monster or just an illusion as the angel claimed in my dream . . .

I made up my mind to try to get out of my body once again but, as a precaution, I planned an escape: If I encounter the monster again, or if other monsters show up, I will immediately get back into my body and under the blanket . . .

I really hoped that they couldn't touch me once I was in the physical reality and well-covered with my blanket.

Then I decided to start with the relaxation techniques which the angel had described to me the last time I had been with him in his reality. I remembered it clearly, but first repeated to myself the important steps:

Relax, close your eyes and count backward from ten to one . . . using the special relaxation steps. Put all of yourself in the upper part of your head, then be one with the heartbeat as if you are the heart and nothing else. Once you feel you are the heart, shift your attention to your stomach . . . be the stomach. Then shift your attention to your feet. In every part or organ of your body that you put your attention on, be that part and nothing else. Then move to other parts . . . from the feet move your attention to the legs, then to the pelvic area . . . continue up to the stomach again . . . to the heart . . . to the throat . . . and then . . . to the center between the eyes. Next, move into the top of the head . . . stay there for a few minutes . . . try to feel vibrations in your head . . .

Once you feel the vibrations in your head, which are actually energy patterns of the Universe reaching your mind, you can continue now with the same process over and over again until the shifting of your attention from one part of your body to another one becomes clear, quick and easy." Once this level of relaxation and awareness is reached, you continue with the third part of the technique. It is actually the same as the second part, but this time you should remember that you are not your body, but you stay in your body. Be aware of it all the way through and continue to relax. You are not the physical parts. You stay as a GUEST at that physical part or organ of the body. You are not the physical body, you stay in it as if you live there . . . attached to your body. You are your soul, not your body . . . Once you are aware of this phenomenon, you can move inside of the body with your soul, again visiting each part, until the distinction between yourself and the physical body becomes clear to you . . . Now, radiate love. It is the right time to thank your body and promise your body that you're leaving it temporarily and you will be back in a short period of time. In this stage you need to radiate love to your body. Remember, you should never attempt to leave your body without acknowledging its efforts to comply with your needs. Otherwise the physical body might become frustrated, and that might be a cause for future problems manifested as physical or mental disorders.

"You can leave your physical body through one of the many doors or openings of the body . . . sense the feeling in your throat now . . . This is the door for you to get out of your body, David. Yes, the best opening door for you is in your throat . . ." I remembered the angel's words and kept repeating mentally all the steps. They were all perfectly clear to me.

With a lot of fear and hesitations, I decided to give it a try once more. Knowing that I fully remembered the various steps of getting out of my body gave me the confidence that I could do it. I hoped that the angel would be here, once I would get out of my body . . .

I then took a deep breath and started the relaxation technique exactly as the angel had instructed me. Following the initial relaxation techniques, I continued with the next exercises. Now I could move freely inside of my body; the shifting from part to part became clear and easy. I became more and more aware of the real me—the soul inside my body. Once the sensation that I was a separate entity from my body was clear, I concentrated on my throat—my soul's door to the outside. Soon I could see the bright light at the end of it. And within a split second I was out floating above my body again.

The room was full of lights now, but I was afraid. I looked around, just to make sure that the monster was not nearby. Instead, I found the angel in the corner of the room. He was waiting for me with a warm, greeting smile, radiating endless feelings of pure love toward me. Soon I felt completely relaxed. All of my tension and fear disappeared, and the familiar happiness and freedom while being out of the body started to come back to me, filling my whole soul.

The angel kept smiling and reassuring me that everything was now OK. Yes, I was happy again. I loved that angel very much. I wondered how all the anger I had felt toward him during the previous months, after he hadn't shown up when I had called for his help, was now gone, as if it had never existed. Once again it was the old great feeling of being secure, happy, excited and filled with the tremendous love that the angel was radiating toward me. Nothing else mattered.

His presence was a reassurance that from now on all of my questions and needs to know will be solved, exactly as I had visualized it prior to the traumatic encounter with the evil spirit. I wanted to go ahead now and ask the angel about this monster that had scared me so much, but the angel started talking to me first, slowly coming closer.

"David!" The angel's expression now became more serious. "You wanted so much to learn and grow in the spiritual world realm. You have the capacity to do so, but it requires something from you as well. It demands your dedication, persistence, trust and, most important, your commitment.

"You must make a serious decision, and do it now. Your decision today will seriously affect your life. You have a choice. It is either to invest in your spiritual growth or not. If you do, then a commitment on your part is mandatory, with no excuses, even if it is hard or scary. Therefore you must have trust and when times become tough and difficult on either side of your life, the physical or the other side, you must remember your commitment and be persistent with your spiritual training. No matter what happens, you will have to dedicate your life to the spiritual activity. Even if you decide to quit from your future spiritual activities, you still are going to be part of it, David. It is a serious commitment which requires a lot of dedication on your part, but there are a lot of rewards which will be awaiting you, and in many aspects you will also be protected by the Divine Forces of the Universe.

"Again, David, I want you to think very carefully, because it will affect your life. It is a very important decision which you must make. Nothing is really forcing you to make this kind of serious commitment, not even I—nothing but your own decision. I'm just presenting it to you for your own consideration. Only your spiritual needs and willpower to continue practicing should dictate your decision today."

But, what are my spiritual needs . . . ? I looked at the angel, wondering.

"It is part of you, and your destiny. Just listen to your inner self, David, and you will know.

"Now, let's take a look at the other side of your decision. If you decide not to commit, then, it is also OK. Nothing bad will happen. The spiritual world, including me, will still love you. And regardless of the decision you make today, you will be protected by the Divine Forces of the Universe and your guardian angels. Also, since by now you know how to get out of the body, you still will be able to do so, if that is your wish.

"You see, David, if you decide to decline today's offer, there is nothing to fear or to worry about. In many aspects your life will be much more peaceful. Generally, your life events, your destiny, will continue to be on the same path as they are now, which is mainly as you plan them ahead as every other human does. Therefore, if you decide not to commit yourself to the spiritual activity, the main difference is going to be that you will have a normal spiritual growth, but without further divine teaching. Even for your growth in the spiritual awareness, you do not really have to worry, because you still will flourish in the spiritual realm. So, it is maybe safer for you to decline your commitment today, but before you answer, I want you to take a moment and think seriously. Your entire life and destiny depend on it.

"There are no right or wrong decisions, nor will I look at you differently regardless of your answer. It is not a test, nor an examination like those at your school. It is really the most important decision you will ever make in your entire life."

I was listening, absorbing his words so rapidly, quite surprised at the unexpected offer. He continued with the explanation of the commitment, staring at me as he did so with the same serious expression on his face.

"I know you do understand now the seriousness of your decision today. And I also know that you are capable of deciding on your future regardless of your young age. Others, at about your age, had the same decision to make and did it well regardless of their positive or negative responses. However, I want you to know that most of those young persons who did commit to the spiritual service were able to keep this commitment for life. This spiritual service to humanity has been done for thousands of years and, so far, it has proved to be a valuable tool for the evolution of humanity. But, David, regardless of what others decided, I want you to think clearly and independently according to what feels right for you now and for the rest of your life. Remember, once you decide, either way, there is no turning back. And, yes David, it is a once in a lifetime decision. It's a final decision that you must make now.

"While you are thinking about your response to me, I want you to know now and forever, that: EITHER WAY, THE CHOICE IS YOURS—YOURS ALONE!"

I was confused and overwhelmed by the seriousness with which the angel described this commitment to me. I just wasn't ready for this kind of speech and didn't feel I could commit for life. The angel noticed my confusion, and continued in a much softer voice, "David, before you give me your final answer, let me clarify the commitment I am asking you to decide on now.

"You can be a great helper in the world, move and advance the life process of humanity further into a better future but it is up to you. It is your decision. No one will force you to do anything you do not want to do, but there is a commitment and then a process for you to grow and become a successful helper within the Divine Forces of the Universe, which are those who help humanity with the reincarnations and the evolutionary process. Also you must know that if you want to reach your spiritual expectations, then you must invest in the serious training it requires."

But what kind of spiritual expectations does he mean . . . ? Does he know my inner self better than I . . . ? Probably he does . . .

"David," the angel continued, "I know you feel too young now, and this type of commitment seems too early. Nevertheless, this is the right time for you to decide. There is no need to delay your destiny. You must reach this mature decision now. We cannot train you without your commitment. The right time to start is at your age.

"Believe me, David, it is your destiny which requires me

to ask for your decision in this final way. It has been presented in the same way for many thousands of years on planet Earth and other planets as well, where humans and other intelligent beings are in the physical form."

"... real humans on other planets?"

"Yes, David, on many of the star systems in yours and other galaxies, but for now listen very carefully. As you know, I am repeating myself so you will understand the offer completely. If you decide to take my offer, then you must follow your decision which is final. Yes, David, even at times when it is scary or unpleasant. And there will be times when you will have other types of feelings besides happiness and fulfillment, experiencing some events which might be difficult for you. But again, at those difficult times you must remember your decision of today and keep going with your spiritual commitment, no matter what happens, and no excuses. It is a commitment for life. Maybe it is hard and demanding in many ways, but also rewarding. There is a lot of satisfaction when you can help others to successfully continue in the evolutionary cycle of humanity.

"For most of the people on Earth, whom you call humanity, this opportunity to become a spiritual helper is practically impossible. There are many reasons for it. In due time you will know more about it. During the centuries quite a few have had this training. Some of them became very well known and have helped humanity in various ways. Some others, although they were very capable persons, failed in their commitment and, therefore, in their spiritual growth.

"There are many reasons for the question of why some people become successful and prosper in life, while others with the same talents and capacities fail. David, remember that among the most important reasons for success as a spiritual helper, are trust, determination, commitment, devotion and destiny. It is the true secret for the success of everyone including those of the spiritual helpers. You have control of those characteristics and, to some extent, you can influence your destiny as well.

"David, no matter what you decide, whether you will join the spiritual helpers or not, you have the talent and capacity to reach your goals. The rest is up to your own efforts and that's including the growing in the spiritual reality. It is really up to you. And remember, if you decide to commit, your real training will start now and continue while you learn at your marine boarding school, then it will proceed throughout your lifetime. You will have many friends and girlfriends and, eventually, you will get married, but even at those times, you will have to keep up with your commitment. It is a commitment for your entire lifetime.

"Yes, David, if you decide to commit to the spiritual training, then you will have to work much harder than most of your cadet friends. You will have to practice mainly after school hours and social activities, and be very clear with determination to grow in the spiritual reality. Do not worry. You will complete your high school successfully and with honors. And while you continue your life, initially as a sea cadet, then as a deck officer in the merchant marine, you will have to comply with your spiritual duties as well, no matter where you are going to be in the world. After that period of time, your life style will change considerably, but it is too early for us to go into more detail of your future.

"David, regardless of your decision, you must keep this offer confidential. If you join us, your spiritual training and the knowledge you obtain in this realm should also be kept strictly confidential, until . . . one day, in your adult life, when you will be teaching a few selected people the principles of the spiritual reality, then you may share this information with others, but first you have to pass the spiritual training and become a helper. It requires a lot of learning and experiences in this realm.

"Once you become a spiritual helper to the Divine Forces

of the Universe, your duties will be simple. You will help people through many types of healing and provide them with spiritual support while they are alive. Then, in times of accidents or deaths, after they pass away to the astral dimension, you will help many individuals in their reincarnation processes. This service is also performed every day by the many angels, guardian angels and spiritual helpers. Other duties and spiritual activities may be required from you, but usually those activities will not take you away from your routine life. It will never be greater than to the degree of your willingness to volunteer and help others in the spiritual reality.

"For now, David, I think you have a general idea of what is required from you, if you do accept the offer today. I do not want you to delay the answer of your decision for tomorrow or another day. THE ANSWER MUST BE NOW. If you choose to join, you must think about your commitment daily until it becomes part of you. Do it together with your daily spiritual training by me or other angels until you complete your training, becoming a full capacity spiritual helper. If you decide not to commit, remember that it is also OK and I will still love you, as always.

"Now I want you to think for a moment and give me your decision."

When the angel completed his speech, I felt paralyzed, unable to digest this news, or actually to reach even the most remote concept of making any decision. I wasn't ready for anything like this. Even though he had repeated himself when I had been confused, I felt as if I did understand the words, but not really the meaning of his concepts such as: "commitment for life." All I wanted to have is a little or a lot of fun in the other side of life, yes, in the floating side which, by now, I knew that people call the astral life, the spiritual reality and maybe some other names. Whatever you call it, for me it was a place for fun and adventures, nothing else, nothing more. Now I realized, obviously, that the angel had not viewed that world as a fun or an adventure world. He seriously related my involvement in that world with a service to humanity. Me servicing others . . . ? NO, NOT ME, NO WAY . . . simply forget it . . . I have enough commitments at school, and who knows what else will be required from me if I do agree to his proposal . . . The angel looks very serious about the service as a helper to the Divine Forces . . . It isn't a joke or a game . . . It is more serious than what I had promised to the vice-principal . . . It is a type of commitment for life . . . He was clear on that . . . it's also unfair because I don't even know what it takes to fulfill his expectations from me . . . and the fact that only a few in the world are chosen for this service makes it even worse, because that means it is really a difficult task . . . Besides, the angel did promise that nothing bad will ever happen to me if I refuse to commit. So, no problem, it's a great offer, but simply not for me . . . Yeah, I should smile nicely to the angel and then tell him that I respect his offer, but it is not my "cup of tea." I will ask him to stay in touch because I love him so much and, then, see him around when I would, if ever, leave my body again . . . why bother with something so heavy . . . and on the other hand, if I do commit, as he just said, then there is no way back . . . it means to enter blindly into a way of some type of life that I have no idea what it really means. Who is so crazy to do it . . . ?

Thinking on the pros and cons of the decision wasn't easy. I then wondered if any of those who are very close to me would ever agree to such a proposal. I didn't think so. In addition to my confusion, I now remembered my father's discussion, just in the previous month, about contracts and promises in the adult world: "You need to be careful before any contract, commitment or promise is given or signed by you in the future. You must know all the facts, circumstances, then ask yourself a few times the basic questions while considering all the possibilities. Never take things simply because the other side presents them nicely. It is usually done in order to make that offer attractive. It is your duty to verify the various aspects of the offer. You must check first before any type of commitment is given. Remember, David, never promise things that you aren't sure you can comply with. Always ask for more time for a decision, and check the accuracy of the offer. Also, the more serious the offer is, the more you must check the details and be sure you can or want to comply with them . . . "

Yes, I know what my father would tell me to do in this case . . . and no wonder why . . . It is quite absurd . . . I really don't know anything about the spiritual world with its monsters and who knows what else . . . How can I verify the facts or know the truth . . . ? Besides, the angel is asking me to commit now. So anyway, I don't even have time to check the new offer, therefore the answer must be NO, absolutely NO. My father would do the same . . .

Just when I was about to reach this final, sober conclusion and, kindly, was about to refuse the spiritual offer which, to my opinion, I had carefully considered, something in me shouted: David, think again . . . You didn't take the entire picture into your evaluation . . . David, don't refuse this offer . . . take it, take the offer, no matter what. It is the right thing for you to do . . .

But then another part of me protested; why should I take it if I don't even know what it takes to become a spiritual helper . . . ?

I now remembered that at home I hated to help my mother with the endless housecleaning or even to go shopping with her. This offer might be much worse . . . and for life . . . no way back! No. Not me!

I tried to rationalize with my inner voice, but something in me was persistent, stronger and clearer: David, you are about to lose a once in a lifetime opportunity. You know it will never come again. No matter what it means ahead, you shall face it when it comes. David, take it!

Part of me was almost begging to take the offer, while another part of me simply refused. Then I remembered, again, the experience with the evil spider. The astral realm is not so funny . . . It is a dangerous place to be . . . there are many mysterious monsters, odd spirits, and who knows what else . . . If the angel warned me about the difficulties, he isn't joking. He knows what he is telling me. I'm ignorant in this realm, I'm just a little kid. Who knows how old this angel is . . . ? For him it's not a big deal, but for me it might be a lifetime mistake . . . and, as my father said, for he is a very smart person, I should never commit to something if I don't know or understand, or have all the facts about it.

My decision, was going in both directions: Take it! Leave it! Take it! Leave it! I really didn't know what to do. As soon as my logical answer was negative, something in me would jump and scream: You are losing a once in a lifetime opportunity to fulfill your dreams. Take it! Agree to the offer no matter what!

But what are the realities of my wishes and dreams . . . ? I didn't really know. Then take the offer and find out, otherwise you will be sorry for the rest of your life . . .

But, maybe I won't be so sorry. Maybe it is much better to say no. Maybe life will be more interesting without this commitment . . .

No. Once, you know the truth, it's never going to be the same . . . If you refuse now, you will be sorry for the rest of your life . . . There is no way back David and you know it . . .

Weighing the response on both sides never made it easier. I realized in that reality, I HAD NO CHOICE. If I refuse now, then I will probably never forgive myself for having ignored and lost such an opportunity, even if it would be a difficult one . . . Yeah . . . I'm willing to take the chance . . . There is no real choice . . . I have to take it now, and then face the consequences of my decision . . .

I looked at the angel who was waiting patiently. He was smiling at me now.

"YES, YES, MR. ANGEL, I TAKE THE OFFER, NO MAT-TER WHAT, YES, I AM TAKING YOUR OFFER, I WANT TO JOIN THE SPIRITUAL HELPERS. THIS IS MY FINAL DECI-SION!" I was determined, not really understanding why I did it.

The angel kept looking at me for a moment. Soon I felt enormous loving vibrations penetrating my entire soul. They were coming from all directions. The lights in the room became so strong and bright, and the walls completely invisible, as if we were floating outside, in space. The soft music in the air sounded so beautiful and harmonious now. I felt almost melting from joy and excitement. Something in me became so happy, knowing that somehow I had done the right thing. I had made the right choice to join the spiritual helpers for the Divine Forces of the Universe.

But after a few seconds, although I felt that I had made the right decision, the worry and fears were still deep and persistent. In a way they grew now even more so. I tried to control them and calm myself, but I was afraid, still hoping that I had done the right thing for my future. I had a commitment now, and I felt that the responsibility I had taken by this decision was enormous. I . . . have to focus and overcome my hesitations and fears . . . otherwise . . . I might not be able to function at all . . . I'm strong enough to overcome those fears . . . yes . . . I am strong . . . I was trying to convince myself and calm down, but deep inside me I knew that only time would resolve these fears. Anyway for now it was too late to regret—the decision was made.

The angel didn't say a word about my positive decision, or even about my hesitations and fears. There were only the look and the radiation of endless love—a positive approval. As I found out much later, the angel, of course, had known what my decision would be, but he wanted my complete conscious devotion and commitment to the spiritual training for becoming a spiritual helper.

Well . . . now that I'm committed and have promised to dedicate myself, my entire lifetime, to this spiritual service, then what should I do next . . . ?

As if I were thinking aloud, the angel responded with a loving smile, "Now that you are committed, and I have your promise to take the training seriously, we can continue. You shall learn about the spiritual reality, the ten levels of existence in the Universe, what your role will be as a spiritual helper to humanity, why we need this type of service, what is life, why you live and what for, and what is the future of humanity. Also, you will be introduced to the many life forms of the Universe and meet other great people who, just like you, since a young age, have dedicated their lives to become spiritual helpers within the Divine Forces of the Universe and to help humanity. Almost all of them, when they were offered this unique, once in a lifetime opportunity, were initially afraid and had a lot of worries and hesitations. Nevertheless, they decided to join the Divine Forces. Also, similar to you, they were in doubt, but regardless of their fears and hesitations, they took the offer. David, you will find later that this offer is given to only a few people in each generation. To become a spiritual helper, one must possess a high energy intensity soul, and other qualities in the personality which are required for this sensitive activity. We call these volunteers 'the spiritual helpers,' 'spiritual helpers,' or just 'helpers.' Right now you are considered as a 'junior helper.'

The angel paused for a moment. I wanted then to ask him about the nature of my future activities, the requirements or the duties that I will have. I also wanted to know if we could meet with the other helpers right now, but the angel ignored my unspoken questions, and before I could ask anything, he just continued with another issue which had bothered me before this meeting.

"Now, David, I want you to go back into the problem you

encountered with the illusion—the one you call the monster, evil spider or the evil spirit. Think for a moment. Why aren't you afraid to die, but are afraid of a scary spirit that looks like a monster? What can seem worse to you than death itself?"

I didn't know what to answer. A few responses were in my mind, but I wasn't sure I had the right one. Better keep silent . . .

"It is OK, David. I do understand perfectly your feelings, but do not worry, you always can be open with me and tell me what you think or feel. I am here for you. Remember it. So you do not really have to choose the nonresponse when you are not sure of the truth or the correct answer. Feel free to talk to me anyway. My question was to open your eyes into the nature of fears. Remember, fears are only thoughts or events that have never been fully processed in the mind. That is what all fears are about. Ideas, thoughts, things or events might be sad or happy, good or evil, but fears are the incomplete process.

"You can process your fears to their natural end, simply by asking the question 'what if . . . ?' Then answer it. Next, ask again 'what if . . . ?' And again answer it, until you process the entire thought to its conclusion. And once you do it correctly, without avoiding segments of it, then normally the fear will disappear. Later on in your training, you will learn some simple techniques for overcoming fears and, especially, the fear of death, of suffering pain, misery, or of suffering from emotional frustrated love or separation, for whatever reason, from a specific person or even an animal. These are a few of the ultimate fears in humans.

"You know, David, very soon you will be able to laugh at the various illusions and misconceptions that people of all ages and backgrounds have, especially fear without any reason, or, just because someone with a specific interest to control them wanted them to stay in the fear state. All of these many people, for many reasons, never processed their fears to their ends.

"Now, in your case with the 'monster', it is completely

understandable and actually natural. Therefore, we have to talk about it."

I was listening very carefully to every word of the angel. It seemed to me then that they were said at an enormous speed, but somehow in that dimension, out of my body, I was able to conceive them as fast as they were said. It seemed to be a normal speed of conversation between two individuals.

The angel continued, "The astral world is different from the physical world. There are usually no violent attacks on each other, even with the really big entities that you may call monsters. They will not attack you in this realm as you might expect in the physical reality. Does it make any sense to you?"

"No, I don't really understand it, but nothing anymore makes sense to me. Why should a spirit take the form of a monster?"

The angel smiled. His response was as if he were talking to a baby. "The reasons for that, David, are many, but in reality, that small spirit simply enjoys scaring others. This phenomenon happens mainly in the astral level. Within the purer levels, for example, those scary things usually do not occur, simply because the spirits or entities have other types of activities which are far more enjoyable, interesting or stimulating. They also have more responsibility toward life, and being in a purer level of existence takes away completely this type of humor which you will experience, in the future, as a part of the astral mentality. You will notice, then, the seriousness of the higher levels of existence in the spiritual realm, versus the 'looking for fun' of the small spirits and some of the human and animal spirits, as sometimes is done within the astral level."

All of a sudden, the angel's words reminded me of the helpless feeling that I had after encountering the evil spider in the astral level and the months that he had never responded to my calls for him.

"Why didn't you come when I called you so many times?" I found myself accusing him instead of relating to what he had just explained to me. Now that I was committed to the practice and service in the spiritual reality I was worried again. I perfectly understood that I would have to fulfill all of my new duties, regardless of my feelings. Who knows if the angel will leave me again, and won't show up when I call for help . . . ? What shall I do then . . . ?

I then remembered to ask him something that had bothered me for the last few months. "You didn't even tell me your name, you know." I continued with my complaints. "I wasn't even sure that you can hear me. I was calling you every night since the appearance of the monster."

The angel smiled at me again, "Can you tell my name now?"

"Upiel?" was my spontaneous response. The angel nodded with his usual smile of approval.

Upiel. That apparently was his name. The idea that I could call him by his own name provided me with a great feeling of relaxation and security. I don't know why, but I assumed that from then on he would come when I needed him, simply because I knew his name.

Next, I began thinking about the spirits in the astral level as the angel had described. I realized my mistake. I should have trusted his instructions and exercises . . . but on the other hand, I was afraid and he wasn't near me to explain or protect me . . . How could I have known that this monster was not real . . . ? How could I have known that it was only an illusion, without him telling me about it . . . ? I wasn't really sure even now that it had been an illusion. I wanted to see it for myself.

"Alright, David." The angel gave me his illuminated hand, "Let's go out for a tour of the astral level. I want you to see it for yourself."

I wasn't ready for this kind of response, especially since I had only thought of this topic. I was also ashamed that he had seen my distrust in him. With a lot of shaky feelings, I followed him through the ceiling and out we went.

The night was clear. A full, bright light filled the whole world. We floated there above the dormitory. For the next few moments, I had the strange feeling that he was actually calling for the monster. I soon realized that it was true. Sure enough the monster was approaching us. Its wide open, scary eyes, were looking with an infinite, cold cruelty directly at me, as if it were going to attack me. I became terrified again, but I didn't freeze. Instead, I immediately floated behind the angel.

Fully alarmed, I watched how the angel ordered the huge monster to stop. The monster stood there a few feet from us. Then in a loud type of clear mental communication, the angel asked the monster to change into its original form.

To my amazement the huge, ten stories high, fifty foot wide monster changed into the shape of a small, sweet, domestic type of a young, delicate cat which came slowly toward me for attention.

I was astonished. "Is that the same creature that scared me so badly? How could I have known who this spirit was?" I asked the angel feeling completely embarrassed.

Then, with a smile on his face and a lot of goodwill, the angel Upiel, answered, "David, never judge spirits by their shape or size. The main measurement tool in the many levels of the Universe is the observation of the energy intensity. So never look at the size of a spirit. The size means nothing. It's an illusion for those who live in the physical realm, and it might be an illusion for the souls who are coming from the physical level for one of the many reasons that souls do arrive in the astral world. You should never count on, or trust, the size or shape in the astral level and some others levels, simply be-cause the size and shape of all spirits even those of angels are so flexible that they can take almost any color, form or size that they choose. Therefore, remember David, there is no real value in appearances. There is no gender to a spirit either. Your size or shape is totally secondary. I know that this issue of ap-pearance is one of the most important things in the physical world. Even the animal and the plant kingdoms use their appearances for hiding themselves, to scare predators, attract their mates for reproduction, or other reasons. But this is not so in the astral world, nor in the purer levels of existence, in the realms of the spiritual world.

"On the astral level, or nonphysical reality, you should observe the intensity and, eventually, also the quantity of energy they have. It is the only way to categorize any spirit: souls, entities, even those of angels."

For me spirits, entities and souls were the same concept, but the angel somehow wanted me to differentiate between the main types of spirits in the Universe.

"As you see, David, spirits pertain to all kinds and sizes of living energy forms. Souls pertain to the spirits of humans, animals and the cells they are made of. Entities pertain to any spirit other than soul. It can be one that is attached or not to physical form, from an atom to a planet, or even the spirit of a galaxy. Ghosts pertain to those spirits who have been perceived by humans on the physical level, whether real or imaginary.

"Observing the intensity of a spirit, is for you, now, the only way to realize if what you see is a real huge spirit or not. You can relax, David. It is easier than you think. There is no need to measure it. This knowledge is naturally within you. Trust yourself, and it will be part of your daily life. Yes, David, in a short while, practically in no time, and with a little experience you will learn to observe everything with ease."

I heard his words, but I couldn't believe that I would be able to do it. The concept sounded too difficult.

The angel just smiled and continued. "David even though the big entities do exist, usually they will never mix with you. They do not have a reason for that. Yes, there are in the Universe some very powerful entities, with whom, my advice to you is simple—stay away from them. Do not bother them and they will not bother you. Again, some of them are so big compared to the human soul that they will not bother even to communicate with you. In time you will learn to recognize them, especially when you advance into the purer levels of your soul. Then you will be able to communicate with them as well. But, for today, leave them alone. They will not bother you, I can promise you that for sure. Also, remember it for the rest of your life: Always analyze the spirits according to their energy intensity. Never judge by shape or size. They are misleading, as you should know by now.

"David, your observation qualities will improve naturally with time. Then you will learn other methods to observe the reality in the Universe including the way to evaluate the energy intensity according to the living units and to know the real power of any life form in the Universe. Be patient. We have more important things to cover first. For now relax. You will see and experience the astral phenomena, and then the more elevated levels of existence in the future."

I was listening to everything he said to me. I felt much better now, understanding more about this strange world full of spirits, but I knew it was only the beginning of a long journey into the mysteries of the Universe.

The angel looked at me lovingly. He then added with a soft voice,

"David, I was waiting for you to get out of your body, virtually every night, but, there was no point for me to push you into exercises. Unless you are committed to your personal growth, no one will help. People get help only when they help themselves.

"Tonight, during your sleep, you did open yourself subconsciously toward the astral communication. Then the door to your spiritual communication opened. Therefore, I did establish a communication with you. I was actually responding to your request. Remember, usually in the spiritual world, the best way to communicate with me, or others within my level of existence, is to get into my level of existence, or at least—since you will not be able to do that—try to reach to the highest level you can go. Initially I am here in the lower level, which you humans call the astral level, or some even call it the physical soul level. Then you will learn how to advance further into the higher levels of existence and this is, of course, only if you continue faithfully with your training."

He looked at me with his shining eyes, reminding me about my decision today.

"You know that I'm going to practice the spiritual training," I answered seriously. The angel just looked at me and smiled.

Why, then, is he reminding me about it . . . ? I wondered. I'm willing to forget the incident with the monster, and to do my practices as I promised, so what else should I do . . . ?

The angel continued to smile with no reply.

Soon I thought about my next out-of-body training. A similar traumatic incident like what happened with the little cat who tricked me won't happen again . . . I guess it's a kind of joke in the astral reality designed for the innocent souls like me, who dare to visit them . . . Next time, I will start to evaluate the spirits' energy intensities, exactly as the angel told me . . . I should ignore their shape or size . . . I hope that I will be able to do that . . . At this time I have no idea how to look for or to measure those spirits . . . but as the angel stated, the knowledge is already in me, I should trust myself, and I will.

After another few minutes of wondering about the new realities, the angel started to talk to me again. "David," he interrupted my thinking, "soon it will be time for you to go back into your body and get some rest. Tomorrow you shall continue with your training, but you will need to explore the other side of life for a while by yourself until you get used to being in this dimension of life. Then another angel will continue with your training. I will see you from time to time."

I was quiet, thinking about my training.

"Yes, David, your training is going to be fun, but, also there will be a lot of other feelings. It is a real investment for life, or actually for many cycles of life. During your service there will be times of joy and other times of hard work and stress. You must be ready for it with all of your soul and mind. You need this training so that you can be effective in helping others, which is the main part of our spiritual work. Helping humans in their evolutionary cycles is very important work—the biggest thing the helpers can do or perform. By doing it, they also gain more energy to evolve into a better evolution for themselves and for the others whom they help. In the future you will learn more about this topic.

"As I asked you earlier, I want you to keep it confidential. No one should know about your initiation today until you grow and are ready to talk and explain the nature of the Divine Forces. Then it will be up to you. If you want to talk about it, that is fine. But again, I want you to know that most helpers found it better to keep this activity confidential, indefinitely . . . but, again, it is up to you.

"David, soon you will learn what the rules and requirements in the spiritual realm are for you as a junior helper. Be patient. With time you will learn and master all you need to know. For now, I want you to become acquainted with the astral world at your own pace. Then, after some experimentation by yourself and some training with those you are going to encounter in the astral level, we shall continue. I won't be your only teacher. Other angels and beings will teach you, too. Respect them and learn from them as much as you can. There will be a time in your life when you will need and use all of the new information you are about to receive.

"In case you need me, and until you can reach higher levels such as the light level of existence, you can call my name. I will hear you. I promise to listen if you call, and remember, I always will protect you, so never be afraid, not anymore, nor of anyone at any level. If you get fears, then remember to process them with the method I just told you today—using the exploration of the fears with the 'What if?' until their natural ends."

I looked at the angel, I wanted to thank him so much, now feeling much better. I realized that he is telling me that it was time to go back into my body and prepare myself for another day in school. Absorbed with the warmth and light I found myself falling rapidly back into my body, as if nothing really had happened, as if I were sleeping. But in reality I was still completely awake, thinking about the commitment for life I had made . . . I hope I made the right decision . . . With this thought I fell asleep.

* * *

All living and nonliving matter in our
Universe obey the following major forces
which apply separately to every level of
existence. In short, they are the electromagnetic
force, the gravity force, and the two forces of
the atom which are the weak and strong forces
of the atom. Similar forces apply to each
subatom from 1 to 7 . . .

* * *

Life is another force in the Universe.
Life Force or, in short, LF is the main
energy that is found in every living unit.
It describes the intensity, the inner strength,
of any life form or spirit in the Universe.

* * *

6
Astral - My New World of Adventures

The next day I woke up early, totally refreshed, as if I had had a sound sleep for the whole night. I felt happy again and full of such energy as I had not been experiencing in months.

I quickly fixed my bed, smiling to myself.

"Good morning, Joe," I greeted my roommate who had just awakened.

Still sleepy, Joe sat on his bed staring at me. Then, while yawning widely, he exclaimed, "You sure look great today, David!"

"Oh, thank you. Believe me or not . . . an angel came to me in my dream and helped me!" I laughed loudly and he joined me.

I couldn't talk to anyone about my after-ten adventures. First, because of the direct order from the angel to keep the whole training confidential. Secondly, I knew that even if I would tell, no one would be able to grasp it and instead they would probably laugh at me.

Soon my other roommates who had just come from the restroom also sensed a change in me. After all, we were all very close to each other. The three of them had been a little worried about me lately, probably thinking that I had had some problems adjusting to the life at the boarding school which was quite tough and could break the spirits of the first year cadets. Now all of a sudden there was a change in me. They saw a smile on my face, not knowing what really had happened to me.

From that day on, I once again continued to focus on getting back into the tough, full, six days a week marine boarding school regimen which didn't leave much room for dreaming. We had an extensive, above normal high school activity in the morning, and then in the afternoon we were mostly outdoors for the rest of the day, having a lot of sports and physical activity. It included sailing, and a special military type preparation program for the navy. We were all involved in vigorous exercises. Now I felt happy and energetic. It was reflected in everything I did. Once again I liked this routine, knowing that it was preparing me for a great future and would enable me to become a well-trained, licensed maritime officer who could travel all over the world. After all, it was the strong stimulus to join that school and to do my best to successfully complete its intensive 6:45 a.m. to 10:00 p.m. daily activities.

Now, compared to all of these tough activities, I didn't really take the new commitment of spiritual training so seriously. It seemed to me as a type of fun. What can be difficult in a training out of your body . . . ?

Yes, I had listened to the words of the angel Upiel, but had not really grasped their seriousness. Now that the fears of monsters had diminished, it looked to me once again as a great adventure or a game rather than a real study. I was definitely anticipating my new night adventures in the spiritual world.

The last golden beam of the sun sank behind the Mediterranean Sea and soon the night arrived. At about 10:30 p.m. when everyone was sound asleep, I started my spiritual training with the regular relaxation technique, and then I was out of my body again. This time it felt much easier than ever before as if I had been doing it all my life.

Once I was floating above my body, I went straight outside through the ceiling above my bed. It felt as if someone was waiting for me, but no, no spirit was waiting there. The angel Upiel was not there either. I missed him for a moment, but then I reminded myself that he had told me to explore this world by myself for awhile.

Looking around, I appreciated the scene, feeling happy and excited as if it were the first time in this dimension by myself, but this time with no pressure at all.

I started to watch my immediate surroundings in more detail . . . A few spirits passed by observing me indifferently . . . Suddenly I looked at myself and noticed that a long, white, energy cord was connected to my being more or less at the area of my stomach . . . What's that now . . . ? I wondered, and immediately looked down and followed it to see the other end of the cord. It was both funny and strange. It seemed to me like a type of umbilical cord. Soon I realized that it was connected to my throat at my physical body which was down there lying on the bed. It concerned me now very much. Can this cord be cut . . . ? Can it become damaged if I pass through the walls or other obstacles . . . ?

Very carefully I started to float a little higher now, watching my cord extending. Then quite by accident I passed my soul's right hand through the cord, but to my surprise nothing had happened to it. I then did it again—and very slowly this time—but the cord stayed the same as if nothing had touched it. Soon I understood that the white, shining cord had its own special characteristics. I continued to have many questions by now, but, again, no one was there to answer them. I was really discovering a new world by myself with no tools to understand its principles. Trying to relax, I remembered that the angel had assured me that I would be safe, so I really tried not to worry anymore about the cord that connected me and my body. But somehow it alarmed me again. What can happen to me if the cord were suddenly cut by accident . . . ? No, I have to ignore my worries . . . I should have more trust in the angel . . . He would have told me if there was any dangerous situation for me . . . Maybe this cord is another illusion . . . ?

In order to reassure myself, I tried to touch the cord with

my soul's hand again. I could pass through it without breaking or damaging it, exactly as if I would try in my physical
body to stop a light ray from a flashlight. With my physical
hand I would be able to temporarily cut the ray of light, but
once I would remove the hand, nothing would change. The
same happened with this cord, but there was one difference.
With my soul's hand, I could not hide the cord, whether I passed
my hand through it or not. The cord was undisturbed. It looked
to me now as part of my soul, therefore I hoped that I would
be able to pass through obstacles safely without cutting it.

After a few experiments with my cord, I calmed down and
decided to ignore the cord for now, until I would have the
opportunity to ask the angel about it.

Soon I started to observe the clear, bright light that filled
the whole world around me. It was the same one that had
drawn my attention at the previous times I had been out of my
body, but now I tried to find its source. There was a constant
illumination of a bright, white light with a little golden tone in
it. I could clearly read quite far from where I was any signs on
the dormitory buildings.

A light without an apparent source—where is it coming
from . . . at night . . . ? I wondered. Nevertheless, the light was
stronger and brighter than that of daylight. Is it coming from
the sun . . . ? No, it is impossible . . . the sun is now way under
the horizon . . . the moon does not have such powerful illumination . . . Well, this is another mystery here. The angel probably knows the answer . . .

Now, going on with my tour, I suddenly felt like a creature in the middle of the ocean surrounded by plankton and
the many life forms. Yes, now that I was looking for it in this
dimension, the world was full of spirits. By now they were not
so scary. I started to watch them carefully. There were so many,
I estimated by the millions, floating and gliding; some of them
in a slow motion, and others at an incredible velocity as if they
were traveling with the speed of light. It was amazing to me

that I could observe all these with such ease and clarity. What is their real speed in this realm . . . ? I wondered.

Next, trying to analyze the spirits according to the intensity of their energies was a frustrating task for me. I just couldn't tell the difference between the spirit of an animal and that of a person, or even between these two and that of the larger entities. It was too misleading. I could try guessing, of course, by the way they looked, but what if they chose to change their size and just trick me again . . . ? How could I tell?

I was trying once more to observe the intensity of their energies as I had been instructed by the angel, but I wasn't certain about that. There was simply no way to tell for sure. The evaluations I made were confusing me. A few of the spirits that I had categorized as small ones, suddenly appeared as huge giants. I couldn't trust myself in that matter and felt that I definitely needed some more instructions.

Suddenly I realized that many of the students I knew from school were floating peacefully among the spirits. They seemed to be in a semi-sleep state. They were staring at me, hardly recognizing anything and made no attempts to come closer or communicate with me. After a closer observation, I noticed that actually they had a small quantity of energy in their souls, but the energy cords that were connecting them to their physical bodies were much stronger and thicker than mine. Looking at my body, which was lying on my bed, I could observe clearly that the part of their souls in their bodies was much bigger than mine. Is that why they cannot function by will here? Are their souls parted into two? Well I knew I needed someone to explain the new reality to me because by now my curiosity grew with each minute of observation. Yes, I need an instructor . . . but where do I find one? Maybe I should ask for the angel to come . . . ? But I need to explore this dimension by myself . . . as the angel told me . . .

Continuing to glide, I now was looking down toward the sandy hills that stretched south from the school and sloped down to the shore. It soon reminded me of the vigorous exercises we had had there last afternoon. Yeah, we had been running and climbing with all the heavy stuff on our backs, leaving trails of deep shoe marks in the soft, dry, silky sand. Lots of effort had been involved there. I remembered how we had been sweating and breathing heavily. All of a sudden, I realized that actually I didn't have to breathe right now. I could do perfectly well without breathing, but the feeling was similar to that as if I were breathing. My soul was quiet. There were no heartbeats that pounded constantly in my chest, but somehow I felt as if I had a heart inside there, just where it is supposed to be. I then observed the sea, surprisingly realizing that I didn't smell its peculiar water scent which always filled up the air, actually I couldn't smell anything. These were weird discoveries. Concentrating on my soul now, one question was leading to another. I wondered about gravity. I didn't feel any weight. How come it doesn't affect me in this dimension . . . ?

Feeling a great sensation of freedom, I floated even higher in the air without much trouble. But soon I was facing another mystery. It was a cold February night outside. I estimated it at 35 degrees F (equivalent to 1 or 2 degrees Celsius), but being without clothes in this cold weather had no effect on me. I felt actually warm and pleasant, but on the other hand I could tell what the temperature was like outside at present, without feeling any discomfort. How come I feel so pleasant . . . ?

By now I really felt as if I were rediscovering the world. Things in this realm were completely different from those in the normal physical life. But even so, I felt totally normal, as I did during the daily routine of my physical life.

It is no doubt a strange world. How can I learn so many things without instructions . . . ? I started to worry again. Yes, I need to ask the angel all of these questions . . . but he told me that someone of the spiritual world will come to me in order to explain all of these realities, so where is that spirit?

All of a sudden I heard a siren. My attention was drawn to an event outside of the school, on the very physical level. Apparently the police were chasing someone in a car on the highway, about three miles away from our school. I was curious to know what was going on. I exercised my will to be with the police car and, to my delight, I could do just that. I could fly over that car, reaching its speed easily, but somehow I didn't feel the face wind against me. I kept gliding above the police car without anyone seeing me. It was a fantastic feeling. I could see through the roof of the car as if it were a transparent material. The policeman was angry. I could sense his fear as well. He actually didn't want to take the risk, but it was his duty. I then heard how he quickly relayed the scenario to someone else, probably in the station. He was asking for assistance.

Now the chase continued in a northward direction along the highway which parallels the Mediterranean Sea at about three to five miles from the shore. In a while I became bored with the policeman and now I wanted to see the other person, the one the police were after. He was well ahead but I could reach him easily, and soon I was floating above the escaping car. The driver was a young, strong person about 25-years-old who had a dark complexion. I figured he was about six feet tall, over 200 pounds. He was in panic. I could sense it, since it was radiating from him. I knew that the person took some type of drug, and by focusing on his mind, I could hear clearly what he was thinking. He was escaping from the police because he had committed an armed robbery . . . had stolen some jewelry from a store that he had just broken into . . . Unfortunately for him the police had been informed through the security alarm of the jewelry store, and the robber had had to quit before taking all of the jewelry which he had intended to take . . . but now he was afraid, because being a jailbird, he just didn't want to be back in there . . . If they would catch him this time he was going to sit for a long period . . . so better run away as fast as he could, without much considering the situation . . . his best solution was simply to escape . . . maybe he would make it . . .

Personally, I was surprised at the lack of morality that person had. His conscious mind was as if in a sleeping state. At that moment I felt that if I could communicate with his conscious mind I could probably wake it up and convince the person that he was wrong. But on the other hand, I was worried. Isn't it possible that if I wake up the conscious mind of a criminal like this one, who looks mean and violent, it might be dangerous to me . . . ? Can't this person's soul . . . be as violent as the person himself? He is an adult, and I don't feel strong enough to fight him or even talk to him . . . Let him have his own destiny . . . It is none of my business . . . I'm not trained as a security officer nor as a policeman . . . yes . . . I should stay away . . . it is none of my business . . . I tried to convince myself, but on the other hand something in me protested . . . David . . . it is your duty to help humanity and justice. Here you have an opportunity . . .

Yes, I guess it is my duty to help humanity . . . maybe this is one of the ways I'm supposed to help . . .

Remembering my commitment was an indication that I should be involved in this incident, therefore I decided to interfere, no matter how dangerous it was going to be for me. My plan was to try to enter into the head of that criminal and convince him to stop the car and give himself up to the authorities. But then entering into that person's head, I encountered a strong reaction of hostility. His soul was telling me to get out and fast. At the same time, the robber took out a loaded handgun, getting ready to shoot the policeman who was getting closer by now. "NO, Don't do it!" I shouted and tried to stop him, but unfortunately without any results. The robber's subconscious mind was not cooperative.

Not knowing the correct way to handle this situation, I got very excited and tried to get more support for my activity from my physical body. It was wrong decision, just a mistake. In a split second I found myself falling back into my body in a very unpleasant way. Next, I was lying on my bed, eyes wide open, still shaking from the experience. I wanted to go back there immediately, but I was too stressed for another attempt to leave my body. Feeling sorry for that policeman, I knew I had tried my best. The rules or the secrets of the astral reality were still unclear to me. I really didn't know how to get help there yet. While trying to relax myself I fell asleep until the waking call in the morning.

All day long I was anxious to get back into the astral world. Nevertheless, I concentrated on the study material and on all of the other marine boarding school activities, separating these two worlds in order to function at my best in both.

At dinner time, one of the older cadets mentioned he had heard on the radio that there was a violent police chase after a robber on the highway near our school last night. "How interesting!" I murmured, stirring my hot chocolate with a spoon . . . just couldn't wait to visit the other side again.

The night arrived quickly and the 10:00 p.m. routine announcement "It's lights-off time, turn off the lights in one minute!" was heard all over. It meant, by command, that every one of us, the cadets, had to be in bed immediately. For me it was now a welcome announcement that I could start my night adventures in the astral world.

Soon my roommates were deeply asleep. I was ready for my "getting out of my body" exercise. After a short, routine practice, I found myself in my room, floating next to my body, ready to explore the new amazing world.

This time I left through the ceiling and immediately reached a height of about one hundred and fifty feet above the ground. From there I could see the whole school area. It was a nicely structured school sitting on about eighty acres of well-maintained green grass and trees all around. A heavy iron fence about 8 feet high surrounded the entire place. Along the East side it paralleled the highway that stretched for miles and miles.

On the West part of the school area was the Mediterranean Sea with a small harbor. Boats of different sizes and colors were anchored or well-secured at the few wooden piers of the school's harbor. Viewing the area from above, I suddenly appreciated the beauty of the place. How come I didn't notice all this . . . ? I wondered, being aware that my vision in the physical body was a perfect 20/20 . That had been one of the requirements for admittance into our marine school. But now, in this dimension, it was different. I became aware that my vision was thousands of times better, sharper and clearer. I could see everything I wanted to see in more detail. The dormitory and the other buildings of the school looked somehow transparent. I could see through them. Everyone was, by now, in their beds, including my own body.

Although I had been able to observe some of the spirits while I had been in my physical body, I noticed that every time I visited this astral world, the sky was actually filled with all types of creatures' spirits, human souls and entities which I couldn't observe through my physical eyes. My physical vision seemed to me now as if I had constantly worn thick, dark sunglasses that prevented the vision of the transparent bodies and the sharp images of this reality.

I looked, now, away from the sea toward the open fields to the East, then to the cities on my right and ahead of me. I noticed miles of roads, houses and trees. Some streets had rows of pillars standing on both sides. Other streets didn't have pillars, but they were lighted with the bright light that covered the whole world around me. Observing the cities, I felt an urge to visit my home. I quickly glanced down at the watch next to my pillow, realizing it was 11:50 p.m.

It's about thirty miles away . . . I'm faster in this reality . . . I know I can make it and come back to school in time . . . Yeah, let's do that!

I was about to float rapidly above the main highway that leads to my city, but to my great surprise, within a split second

I was home in my room at my parents' house. Wow . . . just incredible . . . I looked at my old wall clock it was still 11:50 p.m.! It happened instantly. . . How can I be home so quickly? What is my maximum speed in the astral world . . . ? The angel probably knows . . . I concluded and then immediately went to see my parents.

They were awake, apparently having a serious talk at the small kitchen table. My mother was chewing a sugar cookie, and my father just sipped from his big cup of tea. Soon I realized that I was the topic of their serious conversation.

My mother was angry. "He is not used to all this."

"Just don't worry. This is the right place for him." My father tried to calm her down.

"With that military discipline? Do you know the children in his class are required to swim in the sea during the winter? No one cares if he is cold or tired!"

"Yes, but endurance can make people better, and especially can help a boy who is unique like our son to reach his best. I'm happy for him. Trust me. It's a good place for him."

"Yeah, if they don't die during the process."

"He'll be fine."

"Come-on, he is only a small kid. Why don't we send him to a regular high school nearby? He has time for all this crazy atmosphere. Anyway he will join the army after high school like all of his other friends here, and then he will have plenty of opportunities for endurance there. It is silly. In other places in the world he would go from high school directly to a university without all of this endurance . . . who needs it at all?"

"Listen, Mom, it is my right to learn where I want. You cannot stop me from exploring the world." I tried to participate in the discussion, but, unfortunately, neither of them could hear me nor see me.

"You know he did choose that boarding school by himself, don't you? He has always, since he was a baby, wanted very badly to explore the world."

"Alright, Dad!" I patted him on the shoulder, acknowledging his support, but he didn't even look at me.

"My baby . . . so instead of being a doctor he will be a sailor. Is that what you want?" My mother was crying now.

"Bertha, David has always had his own ways. Now he aims to be a sea officer and visit the world. I believe he will do it. I respect that boy. He has a personality. You remember how I used to tell you not to worry when he brought home bad grades from school? But you see now that I was right. When he wants, he is an "A" student."

"Who knows what he will want to do next. My baby . . . " she cried again covering her face with her hands.

"Let's go to sleep now, Bertha, you've had a long day, dear."

My mother started to clean the table. And my father went to prepare some documents that he probably had to take with him to work the next morning. It started to get boring. I decided to leave now.

"Good night, Dad! Good night, Mom!" I felt obligated to say although I knew they didn't hear me at all. Then I went out through the north wall that bordered my father's desk.

Gliding fast at about a hundred feet above my parents' house, I took a look at the city below. The little streets . . . rows of houses and apartment buildings . . . the trees . . . the fields . . . I suddenly realized that I don't have any fear of heights, yes, for the entire time I was not afraid of falling down. How come . . . ? I must ask the angel about it, too. Soon I recognized the public swimming pool—my second home during the summer times. Suddenly, I missed it and the memories it held . . . Natasha . . . yes . . . I have to see her . . . I promised her I would one day . . . It has been more than a year . . .

I could visualize her so vividly in my mind. But I didn't have the slightest idea where she lived now, and whether they had returned to our area or not. I decided to try to exercise my will again.

It worked! In a split second I was in a bedroom of an apartment building. Natasha was sleeping on her bed which was against the West wall of the room. Perfect face . . . perfect body . . . hidden in light pink pajamas. I assumed she was about sixteen and a half years old by now. She was sleeping on her right side. I then quietly entered between her and the wall so I could be closer to her face. She didn't notice me at all. I felt like waking her up, just to talk to her again, but knowing that people cannot see me while in the astral state, I gave up and stayed close to her for a while, just looking at her beautiful face.

Then, observing the room, I soon noticed that her young sister who was about four years old now, was sleeping in the same room. She was in the opposite corner, just by the other side of the wide window that separated the two beds. Her eyes were closed and she also seemed to be deeply asleep.

But all of a sudden she woke up. She looked frightened and within a few seconds, she turned her head directly toward my direction as if she could see me clearly. I was surprised, still staying next to Natasha. But the little one didn't remove her eyes from me. I wasn't sure anymore that she couldn't see me. I then floated above Natasha's bed. The little girl's eyes rolled up with fear, following me to every corner of the room. Her mouth was wide open. I knew what she was about to do.

"Shhh . . . It's OK. Don't be afraid." I tried to calm her down. But by now, she started to scream loudly, with a high-pitched, siren type of a cry.

"Mommy . . . ! Mommy . . . !"

I did nothing bad to her . . . It's not my fault that she cries. I reassured myself. Then I heard her parents rushing from the other room. Soon I disappeared through the window of the 4th floor apartment building and stayed floating near it by the outside wall, waiting to see what was going to happen next. I then quickly glanced around. The city looked familiar, yes, it was located west of my hometown. Now I was floating in the air at about forty feet from the ground. Looking into the room again, I noticed that both parents were there, trying to relax the little four-year-old who didn't stop crying.

"What happened, Sharon?" She continued to cry, looking at the window.

"What's the matter with her?" Natasha by now woke up and was trying to calm her young sister, too.

"David . . . from Natasha's photo album . . . " She cried and pointed toward the window.

"Who?" Her mother shouted. She didn't like to hear my name at all.

"David . . . he was in Natasha's bed." Natasha's mother stared directly into Natasha's eyes now.

"Next to me?" Natasha laughed with embarrassment and hugged her sister.

"Yes, then he flew in the room," she murmured, pointing to the ceiling, still crying.

"It's just a bad dream, honey!" The mother assured her little daughter.

I'm not a bad dream . . . ! I felt like responding to her. Then I kept watching them through the wall, still surprised about the idea that probably I had been seen by someone on the physical level. But no one believed the little girl, not even Natasha. They all thought that the kid really had wakened up from a dream. The family dynamics evoked my curiosity now, and I stayed to listen.

In a while everyone went to sleep, but this time the little girl went to sleep in her parents' room. Within a few minutes the house was silent again. Only the regular peaceful music that I had been used to hearing everywhere in the floating world of adventures was still in the background, touching deep inside me. I then felt like seeing Natasha's face again, so I entered her room and just stayed there in front of her bed. Observing Natasha made me both happy and sad.

After a while the idea that I might have been detected by the four-year-old girl woke up my curiosity again. Therefore I went to their parents' room to check if the girl would sense me this time as well. Sure enough, within a few seconds, her eyes were resting on me and a loud, high-pitched scream announced my presence. Now she was pointing in my direction. I stayed next to the floor lamp in the corner of the room and didn't move, but she kept pointing at me.

"David . . . " she cried.

"Where?" Both of her parents shouted.

"There, by the floor lamp. You see? I told you! . . ." She kept pointing at me as she cried. I just smiled at her, trying to calm her down, but it didn't help.

"But there is no one here, sweety." The mother looked at her worriedly.

Soon, her father started to lose his patience. He was tired. "Stop it! Go to sleep right now! There is no one here, Sharon!" Her father raised his voice, moving his hand in the air around the floor lamp. He clapped his hands together. "Nothing here! You see!?" He was right because, by now, I was next to the ceiling on the other side of the room. The little kid was nodding her head, completely bewildered at that moment, not really comprehending how I had moved to the other corner of the room so fast.

Both parents were acting like blind persons. They were totally blocked to the astral reality. Not only couldn't they see me, but they also refused to believe the little kid.

Soon they all lay down on the big bed and pulled the cover up.

"Maybe that creature, David, is dead . . . " Natasha's mother suddenly whispered to her husband. She felt strangely satisfied as she spoke. Then turning herself to the other side, she closed her eyes in an attempt to sleep.

What a person . . . she really hurt my feelings . . . It's unfair . . . I loved her daughter . . . I'm the one who should be angry at her for not letting me be with Natasha . . . I only did good things to her daughter . . . we loved each other . . . I did nothing wrong to be insulted like that . . .

By now I decided to play a little more, and keep them awake for a while. Unfortunately the only one who could see me was the little girl. So as soon as the parents were asleep. I appeared in front of her and made some faces. Soon it all began. The little kid was crying now like never before. Her parents tried hard to reassure her.

"It's a dream! It's just a bad dream, honey!" her mother repeated, but the kid knew what she had seen was real. She really had detected me, and continued to cry hysterically. I didn't want her to cry, but on the other hand, it made me happy to know that some people can see me in the astral world. Then, after a few repeated episodes, the initiative to continue with the game was over. I somehow could identify with the fears of the little kid. Therefore, I left, promising myself that I would call them as soon as I had some free time. Then I resumed my trip to the school. In no time I was there. The place was quiet. Everyone was sound asleep, except someone who was walking outside the dormitory buildings. I soon recognized the security guard doing his routine patrol rounds. He was very lonely, thinking about his wife who had passed away ten years ago. I felt sorry for him and went right to my body. As soon as I entered it, I needed to go to the bathroom. It felt cold in the corridor. "Hello" I waved to the security guard on my way to the bathroom. He nodded, smiling at me. Soon I was back in my bed and immediately fell asleep.

Next day I was waiting for the right time to try contacting Natasha. At 5:00 p.m. there was a teachers' conference in the main office building and we had one free hour. I decided to call Information immediately. Then, within a minute I had Natasha's telephone number in my hand. I dialed it very carefully, hoping that Natasha would answer the phone.

"Hello?"

"Yes."

"Natasha?"

"Yes."

"Guess who's talking"

"David!?"

"Yes, Natasha."

"How did you find us? I missed you David. It has been almost a year and a half now. Where are you talking from?"

"I'm using a public telephone at my marine boarding school. I have to make it short. OK?"

"That's fine."

"You know, Natasha, I was at your house last night."

"When?" she was surprised.

I then told Natasha all about yesterday. First she was confused and just refused to believe me. But than I went into detail with her, describing her bedroom, the color of her pajamas, the fact that her sister went to sleep in their parents' room, the floor lamp . . . everything I could remember.

Natasha stopped me. She was astonished by now.

"David, you have been always in my heart, I still love you, but my mother is determined that we don't meet ever again. I can't fight her. She is too much for me. But . . . can you come visit me during the nights, so we will be together again?"

"I'll try to do it tonight, but I'm not sure you will be able to see me, unless—"

"Unless what?"

"Unless you can ask your little sister to help you with that."

"I . . . will try. She loves me and she is smart, too." Natasha was excited.

"So I'll see you tonight at about 11:00 p.m. I have to hang up now Natasha. Someone needs the phone. Love you!"

"See you tonight, David. Love you, too!"

A boy from the senior class was using the phone now. I decided to make one more phone call, this time to my mother, just to calm her down. Waiting for my turn, I just couldn't stop thinking about the fascinating new world I had entered. Life is great . . . incredible . . . The amount of adventures that are waiting for me are really unlimited . . . I can really be anywhere . . . do what I want . . . have all of the fun in the world . . .

Soon it was my turn and I was talking on the phone again.

"Mom?"

"David?"

"Yes. Listen, Mom."

"What happened? Where are you? Are you OK?"

"Yes, in fact, I called to tell you just that."

"Are you sure everything is OK with you?"

"Mom, I know you are worried about me. But please don't. I'm not cold when I swim in the sea. I like the structured atmosphere of this school, and I'm very happy here!"

"He already talked to you?"

"Who?"

"Your Dad."

"No, I swear he didn't!"

"Come-on, David—"

"Please don't blame him. He didn't tell me a word. I visited home last night when you and Dad had the conversation about me."

"David, I know you have a very good imagination, but enough, I know the truth, I am your mother, remember?"

I guessed I had made a mistake, but it was too late now. I shouldn't have mentioned the conversation at all. She now was furious about me and was blaming my father seriously. I soon had to hang up and return to my class.

The angel was right . . . I should keep my activity in the astral world to myself . . . But I also want to see Natasha again . . . she is my friend . . . to her I can tell the truth . . . I hope it will be OK . . .

That night I could hardly wait for the "lights-out time" order. I finished my homework quickly. Took a shower. Put on my pajamas, then brushed my teeth, combed my hair and was ready in bed before 10:00 p.m.

"You look very excited tonight!" Joe told me.

"Yeah, I hope to have very good dreams tonight." I smiled, looking at my watch. It was exactly 10:00 p.m.

"Good night, Joe."

"Good night, David."

"Good night, everyone"

"Good night"

I was very excited, and fully anticipating tonight. Yeah . . . Natasha . . . she is waiting for me . . . I'm welcomed there . . . I hope so . . . yeah . . . we'll have fun together . . .

I had to work on more relaxation now, knowing that otherwise I might not be able to leave the body and meet Natasha as I had promised her. After repeating all of the exercises, I entered into a deep relaxation and soon I started to feel my soul inside my body. Shortly after, I was floating next to it.

At 11:00 p.m. sharp, I visualized myself in Natasha's home, and sure enough I was there, right in her bedroom.

Natasha was awake, sitting on her bed, while tightly holding her little sister's left hand. They both were looking around searching for my presence. This time the kid was calm.

"Here he is!" she whispered to her sister, pointing at me, but then immediately hid her face between Natasha's arms. I could tell she was ashamed or afraid, or maybe both. Standing in front of them, I smiled at Natasha. She stared in my direction. She was trying hard, but, no, she just couldn't see me. I shifted myself from side to side, hoping she would detect me, but no matter how strongly I tried to communicate with them, it was a one-sided communication. There was virtually no response. I was awfully disappointed. Being unable to talk with Natasha who was sitting only one foot away from me was a frustrating feeling. I also couldn't hug her because the little kid now sat on her lap. Once more I tried to talk to Natasha, but without results. Desperately, I then decided to perform a type of deaf communication with her little sister, but it didn't work as well. I wasn't sure why. Either the four-year-old didn't want to cooperate or, simply, couldn't see me clearly enough to describe what I was doing.

Natasha didn't talk at all, and now I could feel her thoughts. She was actually afraid, more in fear than her little sister. For Natasha I became now the symbol of the forbidden area, the place that decent people don't enter. She did believe her sister, but couldn't believe that a normal boy can do what I did. I felt her love toward me, but also a lot of fear and rejection. Nothing I did to calm or relax them helped. I was totally helpless. It made me sad and angry at the same time to know that my presence alone, without anything else, could cause such fear, especially in someone whom I really love.

During about half an hour, I made all of the efforts and did all of the tricks I could think about in order to communicate with them, but with no results. All of a sudden I was alarmed . . . I must get back to my body immediately . . . someone is about to shake my body at the boarding school . . .

In a split second I found myself back in my bed, and indeed, it was a true alarm. Someone was pounding on the door. The announcement that followed was quite routine by now. As part of our military training, we all were required to be outside within the next five minutes, fully dressed and ready for some vigorous night activity. I jumped out of my bed, still feeling completely alert after the night's traveling. Within a short time we were all outside in the dark, cold weather. Yeah, we were not sure if we would be ordered to jump into the cold water of the sea for a long, night swim, have to start four miles of running, or some other kind of vigorous night exercises. Although most of my classmates looked annoyed, no one really complained. This was just one of the routines here. We lived with that, guessing it was somehow done in many other military type boarding schools all over the world. Soon we were in the middle of our four-mile run along the shore. The

Mediterranean Sea looked dark and quiet tonight. Only the lights of a few fishing boats were flashing far out on the dark horizon. The gentle sound created by the waves was relaxing and somehow softened the sounds of our heavy shoes, which were rapidly stamping along the wet, packed sand near the water's edge.

We kept running as a group in two long parallel lines, breathing rhythmically. The fresh smell of the salty water was everywhere in the air. During the running I thought about my visit to Natasha. It frustrated me, but I was happy that I could see her and I still had some hopes.

Soon we heard the command to turn back. Heading toward the lighted pier of our boarding school, I was totally hot and sweating, just as was everyone else. Then, staring at the cool water of the sea, I felt an urge to jump into it without my heavy clothes on and just swim toward the horizon. I couldn't do much about it. But it was nice to imagine it while running . Soon we were back in our rooms and had to go to sleep immediately after taking a quick shower. No one could tell whether we would be left to sleep quietly until the morning or would be awakened again for another sudden night exercise. It had occurred many times before.

Just as I closed my eyes, I remembered the alarming, sudden sensation in Natasha's room and I felt like thanking my body and soul for alerting me to get back in time. But some "what if?" questions kept floating in my mind until I was sound asleep.

Next morning we were all exhausted from the night training. But somehow I realized that the out-of-the body adventures didn't really tire my body. Although I obviously had less sleep, compared to some other times when I had a long night's sleep before and after similar activity, I felt pretty refreshed when I woke up in the physical world. I must ask the angel about it, too . . .

I was waiting for the day to pass by, so I could continue with the astral life. The day went by slowly. As usual now, I found myself very focused during the class time and totally observing the lectures, even the more boring ones. I knew that most of the teachers had considered me a good student and I was happy about that. Failing here meant attending a regular high school and forgetting about my dreams to travel around the world as a sea officer. The last night's visit to Natasha, and the frustration of not being able to communicate with her, only made it clearer to me now that in the astral world I was only an observer who couldn't really participate. The combination of both worlds' adventures should be the perfect solution for my desires. Therefore, I was intending to continue complying with all of my duties at the school as a cadet, and to be the best I could be.

Late afternoon that day I tried to call Natasha, but it seemed to me that she didn't want to answer the phone although I sensed she was at home. I kept calling her several times, with no response, then gave up and returned to my school activities, wondering whether the visit to her had reinforced our love or had done the opposite. Should I continue to fly there? Would she be happy to see me . . . ? Maybe not . . . ? Maybe it is wrong to penetrate her life in this way . . . ? Was she offended by me . . . ?

I surely hoped that was not the case, but who knows, maybe. Judging according to the fear she had radiated during my visit the previous night, I suspected that somehow Natasha was afraid of my presence. Well, I decided to relax meanwhile, and to find out the truth tonight, once I would be in her place again.

The night arrived and soon after the darkening of the dormitory, I started with my exercises and out of my body I went. Then, just as I had done the night before, exactly at 11:00, I went straight into Natasha's bedroom. She was there sitting on her bed together with her little sister, same as yesterday. The little girl detected me immediately and notified her older sister. She wasn't frightened anymore. Somehow she had gotten used to my presence. I was now focusing on Natasha's feelings. It was painful for me. I could sense the rejection toward me on her part. It was as if she wanted me to visit her but, at the same time, wanted me to disappear, maybe even not to exist. It was quite offensive. Nevertheless, I tried to communicate with both of the girls but with no results. Then I announced to them that I was leaving, not even knowing if they understood me at all, and quickly took off, completely disappointed.

It didn't feel fun to be ignored that way. Next, floating above the city with many other spirits who didn't try to communicate with me either, I had a terrible need to call the angel or find someone else to consult with. Yeah, I wanted to know what was I supposed to do. How can I learn in this astral world without instructions . . . ?

Am I doing the wrong things . . . ? Or is this the way it is supposed to be . . . ? I had no answers to those questions, and I couldn't find anyone who could answer them for me.

I must focus on communicating with the angel and talk with him about the many questions I have . . . about my training of which I still haven't seen any . . . I felt that all the experiences I had had led to more problems and raised more questions for me than actually teaching me anything. Remembering the incidents with the policeman who chased the robber on the highway, the unpleasant feelings I caused to Natasha, and even the result of listening to my parents' conversation about me, I felt as if all my out-of-body activities were really a failure. So . . . where do I stand if the closest people in my life don't really believe me? Is that the reason the angel asked me to keep my spiritual activities a secret? Why all of my out-of-body activities ended like that, total failure, leaving me frustrated? Yeah, there were too many things I needed answers for.

I wandered above the cities which bordered the Mediter-

ranean Sea and then returned to my body, falling asleep immediately.

At 6:45 a.m. another new day of vigorous routine began.
That day I still was trying to talk with Natasha, but only in my
imagination. Without the satisfaction of a real conversation, it
looked to me so empty. But remembering her rejection and her
fears of my presence made me decide not to call or visit Natasha
ever again. I don't need her rejections . . . I will find another
girlfriend . . .

Day followed day. The school activities were, now, too
demanding. There was no time for speculations about the other
side and certainly not for long daydreaming. The theoretical
and the practical classes, the lab workshops, sport and maritime activities were structured with a high intensity and a lot
of mental and physical requirements from all of us. The participation of the cadets became so high and in such a way that
I had to focus myself and do the best I could. With such an
intensive program, there was simply no time for anything else,
other than for the actual program of study which included the
maritime and military training. Soon the days became even
more condensed since we were introduced to the sailing boats
which were much more fun than the row boats. With these
new boats we began to sail for longer distances along the coast
of Israel. Observing the blue sea, I used to wonder whether
one day I would be able to get all the answers to my many
spiritual questions. And each night, when everyone fell asleep,
I kept practicing my out-of-body exercises, exactly as I had
promised the angel, thus keeping my part of the commitment.

7
Feeling the Pain of Death from Both Dimensions

One night after an extremely tiring, long day that left me and all of my classmates with sore muscles and bones, I found it difficult to focus on getting out of my body. Exhausted, I meditated for a while trying to wander again inside each part of my body, but then I fell asleep in the middle of the process.

Suddenly, at 3:25 a.m. I woke up feeling as if something was wrong. The alarming sensation filled my whole being. There was work to do. Still tired and a little thirsty, I recalled that I actually had fallen asleep and hadn't practiced tonight. How can I prevent myself from falling asleep while meditating . . . ? I wasn't sure. However, I decided to ignore my aches and comply with my commitment.

Soon I entered into a deep relaxation, visited each part of my body, radiated love and reassurance and promised to return to it in a while. Within twenty minutes I found myself floating near my body. The change was radical. I wasn't tired, sore or thirsty anymore. Fully energetic, I observed my body which was lying straight on the bed and I wondered how come I didn't feel even a bit of soreness or thirst. Suddenly, the alarming sensation hit me again, but now it was more intense. Something is happening . . . someone's life is in danger . . . nearby . . . who? . . . where ?

With this sensation I immediately left through the ceiling and from about a height of four hundred fifty feet, I rapidly checked the school area and the surroundings. Then I screened the distant areas. Looking at the highway that parallels the

137

sea, I immediately knew that the source of the alarm was coming from that direction. Soon I noticed that a line of cars was standing along the road. Farther, there were two ambulances and three police cars flashing their blue and red lights all around. It looked to me as if a serious car accident had happened there not long before. Certainly this is the cause of the alarming sensation in me . . . But why did it shake me like that? After all it is not the first accident that I have been aware of . . .

A clear call for duty was heard inside me, the source of which I couldn't understand. What duty . . . ? What should I do . . . ? I really don't know anything of value to help in an accident, not even how to perform basic first aid . . . The brief explanations that my father gave me a few years ago: "Check for breathing and bleeding, don't move the person and then call for help," is not relevant . . . the paramedics are already there, so what else can I do . . . ? I found myself speculating as if I were inside my physical body. The feeling was so intense now as though there was something I had to do or to participate in. So far, from the time these kinds of inner sensations had started to be evoked in me after the drowning at the swimming pool, they were amazingly accurate. It had been hard for me to explain these phenomena at first. Now I began to realize that I gradually had become more tuned to my own inner wisdom somewhere at the deepest levels of my soul. I could hear this inner voice more clearly when I was at the astral level.

My curiosity drew me immediately to that place and, in no time, I was there. The accident had taken place at the intersection about five miles from the school's main gate. Looking at the scene on the highway, I could tell for sure that the accident had happened a few minutes earlier. The three vehicles involved in the accident were still in odd positions, with their drivers inside them. The policemen and paramedics were working hard to release the drivers from two of the three vehicles which were involved in the accident.

All of a sudden, I noticed the spirit of a young lady in her early twenties standing next to a smashed red car. She seemed completely confused while she was observing a body that was crushed in the ruins of the car. I looked in that direction myself. I was startled. Down inside what was left of a red Volkswagen, I noticed the body of a young lady. It was covered all over with blood. The head was tilted to the back, eyes open, and the body was completely crushed from the chest down. Looking at the spirit of the lady again I didn't know what to do, but somehow the whole incident was clear to me now, as if I had been a witness to that accident. At that time I could not think reasonably as to how did I know instantly all the details about the happening. Later I realized that spirits in the astral world do have the ability to telepathically picture the events as seen in the minds of others who were witnesses to these events.

At the time of the accident, Sarah, a recently married woman and a student, had been driving east toward her home. Prior to that, after her evening class at the University of Tel Aviv, she had been working with a girlfriend to complete her final paper which would entitle her to a Bachelor of Science degree in biology. She had been working hard on it. Then, quite late at night after long hours of work, she had left for home. When the accident had occurred, her mind had been busy with the final work which, to her opinion, had not been good enough. Then it happened. She had entered the intersection without stopping or reducing speed. She simply had not paid attention to the stop sign, and since it was about 3:25 a.m., she also had the feeling that no one else would be driving at that hour. That had been her fatal mistake.

I kept looking at Sarah's soul in the astral level of reality. She was no doubt still in emotional shock, looking down at her car and her body with total confusion; not knowing what to do, maybe not even realizing that she was already on the other side of life, and her body was considered dead. I then noticed that no cord was attached to Sarah's soul.

In the distance, I could hear the siren of another ambulance coming to the area. Soon I started to observe the other car that had collided with her. It was an old Peugeot 404, silver in color. Its front and back were completely smashed. The driver, a man in his fifties, was injured badly. There was blood over his gray hair, face and stomach. At the time of the accident he had been on the highway driving south. When the red Volkswagen suddenly crossed the intersection at full speed, there was no way that he could stop in time. His car collided with the lady's car. Now he was also completely in shock. The emergency crews were around him.

Looking behind the Peugeot, I noticed a light blue Ford truck. Its front was smashed. The driver of the truck, a young man in his late twenties, of medium size with brown hair, wasn't injured much, but he was in an emotional shock. He kept his head between his hands, bewildered and frightened. He just realized that he had been involved in an accident that might have killed somebody. He kept saying to anyone around him that he could not stop in time; the red Volkswagen had never stopped at the intersection, therefore it had not been his fault that he had collided with the Peugeot in front of him which had already been involved in a collision with the Volkswagen. "How could I know? How could I know?", he kept murmuring, while holding his head between his hands.

By now my attention was drawn back to Sarah. I could tell immediately that she could not return to that body which was still caught inside her car in a very grotesque, broken way. At that moment, I realized that she wasn't alone anymore; someone had come to help her. Near her soul was a strong spirit made of light, very much like the angel who had greeted me immediately after the incident in the pool. I could tell by the intensity of the energy that he was less powerful than the angel Upiel, but nevertheless he was stronger and with more intense energy than most other spirits I had seen in the astral world. The being of light was patient, letting Sarah get used to her new situation, apparently supporting and relaxing her.

The presence of the being of light was more attractive to me than the physical activity of the emergency crews which by now had pronounced Sarah's death and still were working hard to release the old man from his car.

It felt strange to watch the whole phenomenon from the astral world. It was different from observing the disaster while on the physical level. I was actually witnessing how a person leaves one world and goes to another. From the physical life it was the death of Sarah or the end of her life, but here on this astral level she was a newcomer who joined the other dimension of life. Suddenly I felt I knew that there was a cycle involved here. And she would be reborn one day in a new body. Apparently Sarah knew it as well but she was still confused. I didn't hear the exact conversation between the being of light and Sarah, but I could tell that she was slowly relaxing. However, she was watching her body with horror. "Is anyone going to take care of my husband?" she asked the spirit. The being of light was floating near her quietly and only smiled with love.

Sarah noticed me now but totally ignored my presence. I could understand her. At the same time another soul of an elderly woman in her seventies was approaching our direction. She was gliding toward Sarah with a greeting face as if she had known Sarah all her life. I instantly could tell that this was her grandmother. Somehow, I knew she had just awakened from her rest where she was waiting for her own reincarnation and now came to greet her granddaughter. Looking at Sarah, I felt the excitement in her.

"Grandma Leah!" she shouted, immediately recognizing her beloved grandmother who had passed away six years earlier. I felt strange that I knew this information while I was witnessing all this, even without anyone telling me these details.

It was something that I believed anyone on the astral level could grasp. Observations were my best attempts to explain the many mysteries I encountered without any explanation on the part of the angel.

By now the horror on the face of Sarah was going away, and a quick exchange of feeling was passing between the grandmother and the new arrival to the astral reality.

I kept watching the young lady's soul from a short distance. Then all of a sudden, the spirit of light started to talk with a profound, yet very pleasant voice.

"Sarah, I want you to come with me so that you can see your husband and your parents. I want you to know that everything is going to be just fine. It was your destiny to finish life so early and now it is time for you to complete your cycle of life on earth and get ready for your next reincarnation. You will depart from this stage as soon as you are ready to depart from your beloved ones. Then you will, as your grandma did and as everyone else did, enter into the waiting for reincarnation area. You will be waiting there for your next reincarnation which actually means that, in the proper time for you, you will enter into the womb of your next mother and be reborn. Don't worry. By that time you will forget this present cycle and you will forget even our conversation. You will have a new life with a completely fresh start according to your destiny.

Listening to the explanation he gave Sarah, I was surprised. If we are all reincarnating, how come we need all of these instructions every time we pass away from the physical world? Are we so stupid, or with such a short memory, that every time we pass away we need to be reeducated . . . ? I didn't have an answer to that question.

"Sarah, before we continue any further, do you have any questions that you would like to ask me or your grandmother, Leah?"

Sarah was still confused, I could tell that for sure. Too many thoughts passed in her soul's mind. I doubted if she fully grasped the question. She didn't show any signs of understanding or questioning the being of light whom, by now, she accepted as a super authority without even asking for his identity.

Her thoughts were now concentrated on her husband. The being of light seemed to know exactly what Sarah felt. He then asked her to hold his hand. I quickly joined them. In a split second the four of us were in a bedroom of an apartment. Someone was sleeping on the queen-size bed. One stand with a little lamp was next to the left side of the bed, where he slept. These were the only furniture in the room except for a brown wall cabinet. Sarah floated next to him, watching him closely. I could feel her love for him. It was her husband.

"Josh, wake up! Josh, Josh, wake up it's me, Sarah. Wake up, Josh!" She tried to call him, but he kept sleeping apparently without the slightest feelings or knowledge of the disaster which had happened a few minutes earlier. Now Sarah was trying desperately to call him. She hugged him "Joshy, please. Joshy, wake up, wake up!" There was no response.

I felt sorry for her, but I knew that even if he would wake up, there was no way he would be able to see his wife or communicate with her. They were on two different dimensions now.

Her grandmother came closer to Sarah. "I need to go back into the waiting for reincarnation place. I will see you there. Be well, Sarah." Still in a despairing mood, Sarah listened for a moment and separated from her grandmother who disappeared in a flash. Now Sarah remained with the being of light and me. I didn't feel like a helper now. I was an observer, just a curious outsider, that's all.

Sarah went back to her husband; all of her efforts were now toward him. Soon she felt a deep sadness and the absurdity of trying to call him while he couldn't hear her. Sarah was still confused as to where exactly she was and as to what things she could do in her new state. Other spirits were floating now around Sarah and the being of light, with curious looks on their faces, but not really trying to communicate with her, only smiling reassuring smiles of acceptance. I really doubted if she noticed their smiles or their faces at all. She was too busy trying to wake up her beloved husband. The being of light then stopped Sarah from the fruitless effort to communicate with her husband who was still sleeping, unaware of the accident. Sarah blindly obeyed.

Her husband, by now, was having a nightmare. I could see him moving uneasily in the bed. After a few more minutes, I noticed that a cold sweat covered his face. Soon I realized that his nightmare wasn't a coincidence; it had been actually induced by the being of light who had decided to wake him up. Simply, I thought, because Sarah refused to leave her home without being able to separate from Josh until he was awake.

It took a few minutes for Josh to wake up. He was sweating heavily. Turning on the light of the night lamp, he looked at his watch; it was almost 4:00 a.m. He assumed Sarah was back home by now, and that she was somewhere in the house.

"Sarah?" he called to her with a low voice.

"Josh!" Sarah went happily to hug him.

"Sarah?" he kept calling her, looking at the doorway, ignoring Sarah completely.

"Josh, here!" she cried. He couldn't hear her or see her. Now he became worried and quickly got out of the bed.

"Sarah!" he called with a strange look on his face. "Sarah, are you home?" he kept calling, as he hurried toward the kitchen.

"Josh, Josh I'm here next to you!" Sarah cried, but her husband just walked by her rushing to the kitchen.

"Sarah, are you home? Sarah?" I could feel his anxiety; she wasn't there for him.

"Josh, here, look at me. Please, Josh . . . " she begged desperately, as she floated after him.

They both called for each other. The feelings of desperation were intense now in both beings who loved each other so much. It touched me deep inside. I knew that it was a mission impossible for both.

The being of light and all of the other spirits were watching the whole scenario, but no one interfered. Soon Sarah gave up and just followed her husband sadly. In spite of the late hour, he was picking up the phone and, with shaky hands, he dialed her girlfriend's telephone number. Recalling his nightmare, he hoped she was still there so he could come to pick her up.

"Delia, is Sarah there?" he asked with a quivering voice.

But to his horror, he was told that she had left nearly an hour ago. "She must be home any minute," Delia told him from the other end.

He apologized and then hung up, but somehow deep inside Josh felt or knew the truth. Something was wrong. He started to walk back and forth in the corridor of the little apartment that they had rented a few months ago.

Sarah kept watching him. She was standing by the being of light now. Josh's soul was bonded with Sarah's soul in the astral dimension but, without him leaving his body, there was no complete communication between the two. Apparently their bond was enough for letting him feel very strongly inside that there had been a disaster. I could tell that Sarah, by now, had established communication with his soul, but it was not satisfying. Part of him already knew she was dead, while the logical part of his mind still refused to accept this type of knowledge or be open to the messages from his soul through his subconscious to the imagination part of his thinking. Therefore, he was entering a state of panic. I could feel the attachment and love Josh felt toward his wife, but this time it came together with tremendous fears of abandonment, as if he knew that he will never see his wife again.

Looking at his watch, his helplessness and the terror in his entire being rose. I couldn't tell if this was the result of the inner knowledge which he already had or a part of the normal fear from the unknown. Anticipating, he kept glancing often at the outside door, still hoping that Sarah would be home any minute.

The whole scene was very strange and painful to watch from the astral level. In a way, I felt the intense feelings of both Sarah and Josh as if I were part of that family. It was the first time in my life that I had encountered the fear and pain that death brings to those who remain in the physical world, and the sadness and helplessness of those who leave their beloved ones.

Sarah, watching her husband's terror and helplessness, became shaky. She so badly wanted to calm him, just to talk with him for a little while, to apologize for leaving him so soon, to apologize for not paying attention at the intersection. There were so many things she wanted to tell him now. Her awareness was full of thoughts. Her deep feelings toward him were mixed with a motherhood type of love. Yeah, she cared about him as if he were a child. Her pain was radiating now from her whole being. It was touching. The spirit of light didn't do much. He was quietly watching her, letting her go through the process of separation.

In the meantime Josh's panic grew. It seemed that he decided to take some action. Calling the police, he reported that she was missing. With a shaky voice he gave a full description of Sarah, her car, the time and the direction she was driving. They let him wait on the line for a few minutes, then, very politely, he was asked to come to the nearby police station for further checking of the possibility that she had been involved in an accident or found in a hospital.

I could feel the other side, the female police officer who was at the other end. She was very tired, just waiting to go home. Apparently she got many calls like this one. For her it was simply a routine, but for Josh this was another type of confirmation about the storm that went through his whole being.

Maybe it is just a minor thing, maybe a flat tire, or something like that . . . He tried to ignore it with all his power, still refusing to believe his inner voice. At the same time he was filled with so much fear and pain that somehow he knew the truth—Sarah was dead and that was the end of the loving relationship he was having with his wife.

In a few minutes Josh was dressed, then rushed to his car. He drove toward the police station at a high speed. Sarah, the being of light and I were following him, gliding above his car. I could feel the intensity of Sarah's efforts, trying to protect him from other cars while he was driving. She really loved him and cared for him deeply. If she so loves him, I thought to myself, why then does she protect him now? Why is she not helping him to join her instead? . . . not even trying? Doesn't she want with all her soul to be with him?

Too many things were strange to me. I could feel their frustration and pain in myself as if it were happening to me. I wanted to help them very badly, but I didn't have the knowledge to understand the rules of this world, nor why the powerful being of light did not bring them together one way or the other. There were actually so many things to know about life of which I was totally ignorant. I kept gliding with Sarah and the being of light. But soon I felt as if I were actually a stranger in both worlds; a kind of visitor who, lucky for him, had the chance to visit and participate in real life events and actually be a witness to the many events on both sides of life. It was a cruel and very confusing reality for me. Feeling the desperation of Sarah and Josh at those moments filled my entire being with an intense emotional pain and helplessness that I had never felt before in my life.

Josh arrived at the police station and rapidly parked his car. He rushed in, and then was talking so fast that he was asked to relax first and to repeat his questions all over again. After waiting a long hour, he was told about the accident and then was asked to join a few people in the other section of the building. They were taking him for positive identification of Sarah's body.

At those moments it seemed that Josh was crushed from within. With heavy, horrified emotions, he lost control and by now he was crying and screaming "Sarah!" "My Sarah! Oh no! I knew it! I knew it!"

Sarah was watching him sadly. She understood that she couldn't do much for him. He was in terror, feeling that the end of the world was coming upon him. The heavy fear of "what now?" and, at the same time, he was blaming himself for not driving Sarah to and from her girlfriend's home. Although he knew she would be working on her papers until late into the night, he had told her he was too tired to join her. He really had been. But now the remorse for not joining her was immense. If he had only known. It seemed to me that he was almost going out of his mind. The policeman and the doctor in the examination room were looking at each other. Then the doctor took a syringe with some liquid in it, probably a calming drug, and injected it quickly into Josh's arm, actually without asking his permission. "It will help you. In a few minutes you will be OK."

The effect of the calming drug was fast. I could see the tension and the hardness of his muscles letting down. It also gave him a sleepy effect, but now the tension and fear changed into a deep and profound sadness. He continued to cry, by now a helpless cry, more like a baby's than an adult male.

Sarah was deeply affected by the emotional pain her husband felt. She was trying to hug him and calm him again, to reassure him that she still loved him, that she would wait for him until he would join her; she was not leaving him; she is near him, but what a pity; he does not listen to her; he cannot listen to her.

Then with a painful cry, she asked the being of light, "Can you, or someone else, help me and give him my message?"

The spirit stared at her without an answer, but with a profound, understanding look. Sarah understood from the being of light's look that it was impossible to communicate with her husband.

At that point I was ready to volunteer. I wanted to tell Sarah that once I would be back in my physical body, I would go and give him her message.

But as soon as I intended to do that, the being of light looked at me, and in a deep, loving voice, he told me, "David, stay away. It is not your time yet to help in these cases. In due time you will understand the logic of what you are witnessing in this painful situation. It is not for you to interfere with their destiny. In the future, you will find many people in this type of situation in which you will participate and be required to help, but not now. If you volunteer to translate her messages to Josh, it will delay the evolutionary process for both of them. Yes, David, I know you want to help and it is OK, but you must do it correctly. There is a reason for everything. You will have to know more before you do anything to help others, but don't worry, this is your first exposure to the reality of the helpers. Eventually you will know what it takes to help others."

I was totally surprised. First, since I was sure that the being of light had been totally ignoring me as if I hadn't existed at all. Secondly, because he called me by my name and somehow knew I had joined the helpers; third, I just realized from what he had said that he had been actually in much more control of the situation than I had thought.

I responded to him with ambivalent feelings. On the one hand, I was happy to know that maybe this spirit would help this couple, and that he does care for their best fate. On the other hand, it was a painful situation and the spirit, in my opinion, didn't help as I thought he should have helped. Also, I was glad he talked to me. Maybe he will answer my many questions that I so far had . . . ? But, then, again I felt sorry for Sarah and her husband. Why can't we help them and translate the messages from one dimension to the other . . . ? The spirit, holding Sarah, by now, with something that seemed to me as a blanket made of energy so she would relax, addressed my thinking as if answering my questions.

"David, remember what the angel, whom you call Upiel, told you. Be patient. You cannot have all the knowledge in a few days. Be persistent and you will have all the answers to your questions. Now you are an observer only, so stay in your position. Once you understand the laws and logic of your participation as well as the limitations of the ability to help, then you will have a lot of spiritual work to do. Believe me, nothing is coincidental. Life is like a big puzzle. While we can have some control over our own destiny, it can be done only within the general rules of what is expected from each one of us and again it can be only according to the laws of Nature regarding collective or specific destiny."

I didn't understand much of what he was telling me. His words didn't make much sense to me. All I wanted was to help Sarah with the communication. I felt I could do it since I was still connected to my physical body with the energy cord, while Sarah was not. She didn't have a cord of light attached to her, therefore, I could assume for sure that she was not going back to her body. She was cut from the physical life attachment in a nonreturnable way, so it only made sense for me to help her if I could.

She looked at me as a part of the divine world, or as part of the help she was getting from the being of light. Maybe she assumed that I was his assistant or something of that nature, because she actually never questioned my presence with them. I really didn't know how Sarah was going to react if she knew that I was only an outsider, an observer, that I didn't really live in the astral world, but was only a visitor from the physical world in which her husband lived. I couldn't tell her that, because it was clear to me that the being of light would not allow me to talk to her at this stage. Also, I was afraid to do things in a wrong way, so I remained as a watcher without interruption, feeling sorry for both of them.

After awhile, the being of light took Sarah to visit her parents and her young brother who was about fifteen years old. The parents and the boy were sleeping. This time Sarah, the being of light and I went directly to the parents' home, where she had spent a big part of her life. In order for her to visit her parents' home, the being of light simply took her by the arm. She knew it was for the last time. She would never speak with her parents in their present life cycle again. Then Sarah started to cry without tears, while she was looking at her parents, sleeping together in their bedroom. But this time she made no attempt to wake them up. Only she asked the spirit, "Would my family forgive me for leaving them without a notice or saying goodbye?"

The being of light, with a loving and an understanding expression on his face, only looked at her without response. I noticed that the being of light wasn't very informative at all. Most of the time he only supported her without comment, with a type of understanding look on his face that was actually ambiguous and without really giving her much response at all.

As soon as I thought of that, the shining spirit looked at me with an understanding smile and transmitted to me, "Be patient, David, you will get a proper explanation and answers to all of your questions, but for now be a good student. Carefully observe everything you can. It is not a coincidence that you are with me now. It is part of your exposure to the realm of the astral world, the realm where, as a helper, you will have a lot to deal with. In due time you will be ready but, again David, today it is your first exposure to the nature of life transformation and the place of the soul in the reincarnation cycle, so carefully observe as much as you can. Remember to yourself the many questions you have, because after we complete the cycle of evolution for Sarah, I will introduce you to the angel who will teach you and answer your various questions. Is that understood, David?"

I only nodded. The spirit smiled and then, ignoring me, he continued to deal with the emotional expressions of Sarah. By now it seemed that Sarah was having a wave of memories from the past; part of them I could hear from her soul, but they were not clear to me, as if some issues I could understand while others not. She was dealing with her life events, sometimes satisfied with those events but, many times, she was sad with a remorseful expression on her face.

I couldn't understand why some things that at the time she was happy about, now—by looking back into them—she felt sorry and regretful. I could only guess that her perspective in her new state had changed the way of seeing reality. Was it part of everyone's evaluation of life? Why didn't I have this flashback of my life in my first exposure in the astral world? We are in the same place . . . I'm still connected to my body with the cord . . . Is this what makes me so different . . . ?

Soon I understood that the being of light was actually responsible for this flashback of memories, but why . . . ? What's the purpose of it?

Again the being of light looked at me, now with a reassuring smile, and said, "Good! David. You are a sharp minded person, and you will catch things quickly. Continue to observe this life event and you will understand a lot from it. Remember your questions. You will have the opportunity to get answers for them."

The being of light spent a few more minutes with Sarah, and then without a word, took her hand and led Sarah to the house of her best friend, the one from high school. She was sleeping too. Sarah was now much more relaxed, as if the visit in her family's home had calmed her down because she only looked at her girlfriend and told her how much she appreciated her support and friendship. Then she was ready to leave for her next visit. I was still with Sarah, trying to feel and understand the way she reviewed her life through the soul's mind, but it was hard. Too many things seemed to me just like watching a movie.

After a few more minutes, the being of light looked at Sarah face to face. "Are you ready to complete your cycle of life now?"

Sarah looked at him, then at my direction, acknowledging me for the first time, and next with a type of acceptance for her fate, she said, "Yes, I'm ready. I'm willing to join my grandmother in the waiting area of reincarnation."

The shining spirit then smiled with reassurance and told her, "Now relax. Think about your cycle of evolution and say to yourself: I'm ready for my next cycle."

Carefully I kept observing the instructions which the spirit of light was giving her. Then, as if by a miraculous event, the soul body of Sarah become empty. The remains of Sarah looked to me as if it consisted of an empty nylon bag made of energy, like a cloud. In no time, Sarah and the being of light had disappeared without a trace. Both of them just gone, leaving me by myself, still staring at the place where they were a split second before.

Left all by myself without any preparation, I felt so lonely. There was no one to talk to or to get explanations about what had really happened. The astral world seemed to me, by now, a too cold and unfriendly place to be. I wasn't sure anymore about my part in it. I didn't feel I wanted to visit this dimension any longer. There was too much sorrow. It forced me to witness painful situations and events.

I kept thinking about it . . . if what the spirit said was the truth, then a big part of my work will be dealing with the most painful situations for humans which are death and the separation from loved ones . . . Knowing that I can be in both worlds, and not helping in the way I feel I can, is a source of frustration . . . This is not fun at all . . . It is far from enjoying a good adventure . . . It actually means that I have to dedicate my life to the suffering of humans in the ultimate stages of their pain . . . death . . . Although I know it is not the end . . . still I will have to deal with the pain of after death of these people . . . It is really dealing with the pain from both sides of death, both dimensions of worlds . . . For me there will be no escape . . .

Soon I remembered the pain and desperation of Josh, the crying and helplessness of Sarah, then the willingness to complete her cycle of life. She had to accept her fate as it was, without the power to resist, not being able even to communicate with the people she left so abruptly. This tragedy was too much for me. I felt like returning to my physical body. Once I thought about it, I was back into my body, realizing that it was almost 6:00 a.m. Very soon it will be wake-up time for the next school day . . . With this thought I fell asleep almost immediately.

At 6:45 a.m. I woke up exhausted, feeling totally drained of energy. The contrast between the physical tiredness I felt now and the energetic and sharpness feeling of my soul at the astral level with no need to sleep at all, was amazing.

Only then I realized some more amazing facts about the out-of-the-body reality. If to count my experiences so far, staying out of my body can be an energizing experience or an exhausting one, depending on my feelings while being in the astral world. If I'm satisfied and happy over there, then it also energizes my physical being when I'm back. If I'm frustrated or afraid for whatever reason in the astral world, then it becomes an exhausting and debilitating experience to my physical body as well.

Actually it was a very interesting correlation between the two parts of my entire being which means, somehow, that my soul's activities and my feelings do affect directly my physical body. But how is it really working? I had no idea. Also, it is a kind of unfairness, why my body has to suffer twice when I encounter unpleasant events in the astral reality . . . ? Can I

The more I was thinking of the events of last night, the more I realized that it was not a coincidence. The being of light was right. It was meant to be.

The angel, somehow, wanted me to have a first experience of what it means to become involved in the spiritual activities. Although I had promised him that I wanted to commit to this type of training, I wasn't sure anymore. Was it a smart idea or not . . . ? I felt that my decision to continue with the spiritual training was changing. It surely looked great in the beginning to participate in the highest possible stages of life, or even highest forms of life itself. But when it comes to reality, when I have to participate in the various processes of life itself, it isn't pleasant or fun at all.

Looking at my friends, or hearing them so conclusively talking about their understanding of life, about the reality of death and about what was waiting for them after death, seemed to me so detached from reality, so innocent. Yet, they have their fears as well. I couldn't participate in these types of conversations; they were too childish for me, too boring. On the other hand, in a way, I was envying them for not having to deal with the pain and desperation occurring while in the vicinity of death, as I had to be and had had experienced last night. The case I had been witnessing left me with a combination of pain, anger, helplessness and the feeling of being so ignorant about life. There was much to learn about the laws of destiny. Many questions flashed through my mind. Why this powerful spirit of light didn't help more . . . ? Why the angel, or those great spirits whom I saw, didn't correct the situation and heal Sarah so that she could return to her body and be back in life and stay with her beloved husband . . . ? Why all of this pain and sorrow to humanity . . . ? I didn't have any answers to those painful thoughts and, so far, there was no one I could ask.

In the coming days I became more involved in the school activities. They were so demanding, and for so many long hours, that I did the minimum I practically had to do in order to still consider myself as accomplishing the spiritual training. The days went by, and soon I could stay longer in the astral world but, just remembering the painful situation of the departed soul of Sarah and of her husband was enough for me to go back into my physical body with minimum visits outside of my room.

8
The Universe—Ten Different Dimensions

Time passed more quickly than I thought. All of a sudden I found myself a few months ahead without any real advancement in the spiritual training. I did the minimum exercises every night, but with no intention of getting out of my room or meeting anyone on the spiritual level.

Then, summer vacation arrived. I returned home for two full months. The summer was hot and humid. Many hours of the day I spent in the swimming pool. There, I somehow became an attraction to many girls, younger and older than I, which put me in odd situations from time to time. During these months I had two girlfriends. I dated the first one, Oriana, a 15 and a half year old, for three weeks. She was a nice girl and had nice parents, too. Then I dated Josephine who was 16 and a half years old. With her I kept in contact during the following year. She also had a nice family. Her father was a doctor who loved to sit and talk to me as if I were his son.

During that summer I went to movies, amusement parks and visited some of my old friends from grammar school. I had lots of fun, but somehow everything around me felt different now. I guessed I had changed a little during the first year at the marine boarding school. Now I was more mature.

Late each night I continued to practice the spiritual training in my room, but I did the minimum, just didn't want to be involved in tragedies. The memory of Sarah was enough for me.

Soon I was back at school and another intensive year began. This time our class became much smaller. Some kids dropped out of school. Unfortunately, they didn't make it. Thinking about the dreams they might have had when they first joined the school, I felt sorry for them and wished they would somehow find new goals in their lives.

The days went by rapidly and Spring arrived again. It had been more than a year of routine spiritual training without any special occurrences. Until one night, after I had just left my body and floated next to it, I got a strong sensation that someone was waiting for me outside. It wasn't the angel, I could tell according to the sensations that I received from that spirit. It should be someone else. I was curious, and immediately left through the wall to the back of the dormitory where I felt he was waiting.

Sure enough, a glowing spirit was standing there. Within a few seconds, I could recognize the spirit as the one who had been helping Sarah after the death of her physical body. Now, without the emotional scene, I observed him in more detail. He was a strong spirit with a shining glow of light radiating from his entire body. He looked to be in the shape of an adult man with a grey beard and bright dark eyes. I couldn't tell the exact color of his eyes because of their shining radiation. They were shining more like two strong flashlights, a white light with a little of gold color in them. The spirit had a high, clear forehead, a straight nose and narrow lips. He was about eight feet tall, dressed in a long type of golden gown and wore no shoes. His hands gave me the impression of strength and, at the same time, softness and kindness.

With a smile on his face, he was softly staring at me . I could feel a radiation of love toward me; the type of love that the angel used to show. This kind of love was melting me inside, as if I wished to be protected by it forever, accepting the spirit's wisdom and strength as a much more superior power than my own. On the other hand, those feelings came with a strange knowledge that actually I HAVE THE SAME TYPE AND SIZE OF ENERGY, EXACTLY THE SAME AS THE SPIRIT. YES, DEFINITELY, WE ARE THE SAME . . . That feeling confused me more than anything else; for me it was obvious that I was encountering a superior being, although not like the angel, but nevertheless, stronger than any human being. Yes, I could sense that now, because during the months, I somehow had developed my ability to feel the intensity of those spirits who crossed by the dormitory, and, with time, I had acquired a special ability for evaluating the energy intensity of other spirits, just as the angel had told me I would. It is hard to describe the evaluating or sensing of energy intensity because there was no technical way to measure it, but it was an immediate feeling of knowing. It was based, mainly, on comparing my own intensity to the others. I could tell almost immediately if a spirit was bigger or smaller than I, in terms of energy intensity. Now a strange feeling of evaluating the energy intensity of the spirit who had been waiting for me outside confirmed that I was dealing with a human being, not a superior spirit. Yet, still he was radiating a glow of light from his entire being. I couldn't do that. This was the sign of the superior beings. It was really confusing. I didn't know what to say or do, so I just stayed by him quietly, waiting for the spirit to tell me what he wanted from me.

"David, I have been waiting for you the whole year," the spirit went directly to the point without wasting time on introduction. "I could understand the stress you felt last year, when I had to help Sarah with her reincarnation process. You were a young person at that time and, no doubt, it affected you in such a way as to make you stay most of your time in your room, doing your best to avoid any contact with me or others in the Divine Forces, who are committed for the betterment of humanity.

"David, I can see that you now know how to evaluate the intensity of energies just as you did with me. And you are right. I'm a human being, just like you are, but since I am now operating from the light level, which is the fifth dimension of the Universe, I had to condense myself in order for you to be able to see me at the astral level, where you are now. Therefore, I look to you and others within this level as if I have a special glow of light, similar to the way the angel you met and many elevated spirits in the Universe look, but I'm only a human being just like you, David. I was sent to let you know that you are a very gifted young person with a tremendous potential for developing yourself in the spiritual world and that it is time for you to begin the study with the Divine Forces and to explore the spiritual world more in depth. You will receive those lessons from an angel by the name of Lamdiel who was also my spiritual mentor. He is a very strong and wise angel, but less powerful than the one you call Upiel. Both exist in the third level of the Universe. For a human it is considered a very high level of existence to reach.

"The name, Lamdiel, is actually designed so you will remember his name as your teacher, but, David, remember, names don't mean much in the spiritual world; the meaning of a name in your mind does mean a lot. Therefore, your angel, Upiel, might be called another thousands of names. And as soon as the angel recognizes that the spirit he is in touch with calls him, this is enough for him; he accepts that as if you actually call him by his name. It is the same with Lamdiel. You may call him by this name, and others may call him by many different names. That is OK, too.

"When you are ready, it is time for you to follow me. Just command yourself to be with me and follow me until I will arrive at the place where the angel Lamdiel is waiting for you. In the future I will talk to you again. My name is Ahmed. Originally, I'm from your country, Israel, actually from the Palestinian side, which is the Arabs' side, but don't worry and never be afraid of me. I'm your friend. In our reality there are no enemies between those who serve the Divine Forces. You can consider all of those who volunteer to serve the Divine Forces as a big united family that loves and supports the lives of human beings in general. For us, the only laws which we consider are those laws of Nature as the Creator designed them to be. We, the helpers to the Divine Forces, look to improve the fate of all humanity. For us, all human beings are equal and are the same in all aspects of life. There are no people more valuable nor less valuable. We are all equal particles of the Creator. We do all this volunteer work in order to bring the best in evolution and destiny to humanity. It is for the good of all the people on Earth.

"Remember, there is no difference between people, no matter what their gender, size, wisdom, IQ, race, color, religion, education, political view or any other type of evaluation. We are all the same. You will notice the implications of this important aspect as soon as you become a full capacity helper.

"The main differences in people are in their awareness and belief systems. There are factors which let some human beings believe that they have more value than others. It is wrong and eventually very unfortunate for them. You know, David, the actual bases of all the hate and fights in the world today and in the past, are actually profound fears and ignorance, as the angel Upiel probably told you, and as you will learn more about it from the angel Lamdiel. Fear and ignorance are the main problems which we try to overcome in order to advance humanity into the next, major step of evolution.

"Just remember that no one in our world should hate or fight another. I'm here to help and support you as much as I can. I consider you as my friend or my brother, in spite of the fact that on the physical level you are much younger than I am."

"How old are you in the physical level?" My curiosity woke up.

"I'm reaching my fifty-sixth year of age. For many in the physical world I'm known as an old witch doctor. For others I'm a Sufi. Yet for others I'm a part of the Enteria group, and for you, I guess, I'm a spiritual helper in the service of the Divine Forces.

"Well," he smiled, "whatever you want to see in me, it is fine, as long as you count me as your friend or, actually, as one of your best friends.

"I have been working for humanity as a helper of the Divine Forces for more than forty-two years. So you can imagine how young I was when I started. I was about 13 years old when I first encountered an angel from the Divine Forces of the Universe. Your first encounter with an angel from the Divine Forces also happened at the same age, during the incident in the swimming pool."

"How do you know so much about me?"

"All of the helpers know about you. There are no secrets among us. David, later in your life you will understand."

I was quiet, what does he mean . . . ?

"Believe me, you will be fine. You will be able to reach high levels of existence, higher than most of the helpers of the Divine Forces. Therefore, you will be able to help many people in this world. We consider you an asset to us and to the Divine Forces." Ahmed paused for a moment and then continued, "Now, let's meet with the angel Lamdiel."

I held his hand and in a flash we arrived at the place. Looking down, I found out that all around us was just open sea, as if we were in the middle of the ocean, or actually, the Mediterranean Sea, with no shoreline to be seen anywhere on the horizon. Yes, we simply floated in midair above the Mediterranean Sea with no gravity forces affecting us. I then felt a strange feeling because, although I was sailing a lot now as part of my maritime training, it had never occurred to me to travel above the sea on the astral level.

"Why are you taking me this far? Can't the angel come

straight to my room as the angel Upiel did?" I asked Ahmed.

Ahmed smiled, then replied with patience, "You see, David, when you have to learn new things, we want you to stay focused without distractions from things that happen within the physical level. Since your curiosity is well known to us, the angel Lamdiel thought the best thing was to bring you to an isolated place with minimum stimuli, exactly as he did with me. Also, for you in this dimension, it takes only a split second to be anywhere on planet Earth and we chose the best place for you to learn."

I was happy to hear it, but then, not seeing much activity in the air and not the angel Lamdiel, I started to worry.

"Yes, I can tell that you have become a suspicious, curious, young fellow, but remember, there are no enemies in the Divine Forces. Besides, you are protected by the angel Upiel who actually supervises you twenty-four hours per day all year around. Therefore you can relax and accept your new study. Try to absorb everything that the angel Lamdiel will teach you. Do your utmost, but never worry if you don't fully understand some of the information that he will pass on to you, because those things will be repeated over and over many times during your life. The angel Lamdiel can tell immediately whether you remember the lesson, and then, if you missed something, he will simply repeat it for you as many times as needed until you will understand and memorize all you need to know, including the laws of Nature and your role as a helper for the Divine Forces."

Who knows how intense this kind of study is going to be? I wondered.

"David, don't worry so much. You will be fine. Trust yourself." Ahmed said to me in a soft voice. I looked at him and nodded. I liked him and, in spite of the difference in our ages and experiences, I really felt as if he were my best friend.

"David, I need to leave now. I will be seeing you in the future." He smiled with reassurance and then disappeared abruptly.

I looked around me to see in which direction he went, but he wasn't to be seen anywhere in the distance. It all had happened so fast that I had no way to tell where the spirit had gone. Although I had seen him doing it already, when he had disappeared in no time with the soul of Sarah, it was still a strange phenomenon, even for this fast astral world. That was probably because in spite of the fact that the spirits within the astral level were much faster than anything I encountered in the physical world, so was my ability to follow them rapidly. I had become such a quick observer that I actually could follow the fast-flying spirits with ease, even if they were at their enormous speed but, in this case, the spirit of Ahmed just vanished with no trace of movement, exactly as the angel Upiel had done. Well, I hoped that this mystery would be solved, too, once I start my lessons with the angel Lamdiel.

Then, looking around, waiting for the angel Lamdiel to come, and actually hoping that he would really appear, I became impatient, even a little angry that the angel is letting me wait.

Maybe, Ahmed forgot to call him . . . ? Am I going to meet the angel soon . . . ?

All of a sudden I was filled with powerful energy such as I had never felt before in my life. In the distance I thought I saw the source of it. A powerful being of light radiated endless amounts of energy toward me—an energy shower which was washing my entire being, stronger than anything I had ever felt. My mind became alert as if from a state of relaxation I had drunk a few cups of very strong coffee. My entire being became painfully alert, yet, at the same time, it wasn't scary. On the contrary, I experienced a great calming effect from it. It was the best and the most exciting of sensations one can have. Almost immediately I was feeling more sensitive toward the world around me. It also became clear to me, suddenly, that my level of awareness was now stronger than ever. I felt as if there was no need to memorize or learn at all. Everything became instantly clear in a matter of seconds, and with such simplicity, as if I could know anything I wanted. I wished that I could just stay in this special awareness for my entire life. It was a sensation of wisdom, alertness and of being or becoming a powerful soul, many times stronger than I had been before. Also, it gave me a realization of self-confidence which I had never experienced earlier. All that came as part of the powerful vibrations of energy that the angel was radiating toward me.

The presence of the angel who had just arrived to teach me was really remarkable. These few seconds actually changed and improved dramatically my ability to learn and grow in the out-of-body state. It was as if with a magic touch, my fears of not being good enough to learn about the new reality vanished. Learning anything new became an instant, effortless, pleasant, easy task.

The angel came closer to me now. He looked like a huge, powerful person. All of his being radiated white, pure light like a cloud which the sun is shining through. It was almost impossible to look directly at him, yet he was in the image of a human with white, blond hair and blue eyes. He looked very tall, a height of about ten feet, well-built, with a very nice, well-shaped face; the Scandinavian type, but strangely enough, looking carefully now, I could not tell whether that being was a male or female. I could tell that the radiating spirit was a powerful angel, many times stronger and with much higher intensity than most of the spirits I encountered in the astral world. Nevertheless, the intensity of the other angel, Upiel, was higher than Lamdiel, as far as I could remember and evaluate.

Lamdiel greeted me with incredible clarity, which transferred trembling through my entire being. His telepathic voice was pounding on me in a clear but complex tone made of many sounds. It was in such a way that I had never heard before in my life; like a crystal clear combination of trumpet, organ, violin, piano, flute and other musical instruments at the same time.

It was a pure, musical voice which is impossible to describe accurately, simply because there is not on Earth, yet, such a way to play with a voice and at the same time be able to make it sound like well-orchestrated music.

The effect of his presence and telepathic musical voice, together with the energy I was receiving from him, put me in a totally different attitude. It forced me to completely accept his authority, knowledge and wisdom in an absolute way. Everything from him sounded as a kind of absolute reality. I knew, by now, that I was more than willing to learn from him. Nothing looked ordinary anymore. But on the other hand, deep inside, I was wondering why he was using such an impressive appearance on me. After all, he could appear in any shape he wanted. Even the angel Upiel, who was a stronger spirit, never caused me to be so shaky in his presence. Was Upiel hiding his powers or is Lamdiel forcing me to be impressed by him . . . ?

Lamdiel looked at me, smiling. I knew he had perceived my thoughts, but ignoring them, he went right to the point.

"David, it is now time for study. We will observe the Universe from its simple basis, then, later on, once you grow and accumulate more knowledge and experience, someone else will teach you further. You will learn the more advanced stages of what you will acquire today and in the coming days while you are with me.

"I will teach and explain to you many things which you have wanted to know, also who we are, what is the secret of life in a plain language, the hierarchy in the spiritual world and in the Universe, and the ways to get answers for your most important questions simply by connecting yourself to the wisdom of the divine cosmic knowledge. These answers are possible to get, but only after you have the right technique for asking and receiving information from the universal knowledge, which a small part of it is also available to the human race while in the physical life form.

"David, before we start, I want you to remember that there

is no gender to the spirits, either of human beings, angels, or any other life forms in this Universe. Therefore whenever I, or any of your future teachers in this realm, use the term 'he', it pertains to she as well."

Feeling somehow strange, I nodded, recalling Upiel's comment about this, too.

"Now let's start, David.

"First of all I want you to know where you are in the Universe. It will widen your perspectives and help you relate to the vast amount of information you will be given by me and other spirits and beings in the Universe.

"Right now, as we talk, your soul is in the astral level while your body is in a different dimension which is the physical level. Both of these dimensions are only a small part of our Universe. The Universe is huge. It consists of ten levels of existence, or dimensions, which coexist one inside the other. Seven out of the ten levels are now ignored completely by your science people simply because they don't have the tools yet to be aware of these dimensions. These levels may seem to you on Earth as nonphysical ones. The other three dimensions you perceive as physical. In the future, the scientists of planet Earth will be able to perceive part of the astral level.

"In reality, the whole Universe is composed of three main elements: living units, physical matter, and nonphysical matter; the latter is composed mainly from energy and forces. These three main elements appear everywhere in the Universe but in different sizes, characteristics and configurations according to the dimension they are present in.

"There is a full range of life in each of the ten dimensions of the Universe, but not as you perceive life in your physical dimension on Earth.

"The ten levels of the Universe are not real levels that you reach as you climb higher. These levels are the dimensions which coexist in the same reality and place in the entire Universe for as long as the Universe exists.

"David, let's make it clear to you. Imagine yourself in your room at the dormitory now. You are on your bed, about to start your exercises as instructed by Upiel. Using your body senses, you may see your room, feel your pajamas on your skin and hear the sounds of the Mediterranean Sea, and even smell its salty water if you left the window open. You are definitely now perceiving in the physical dimension of the Universe. But what happens when, with your soul, which is like an energy body who exists in your body, you leave your body? You are still in your room, maybe floating above your bed, but now you are in a different dimension. You are within the astral level of existence. Now you can perceive things that you couldn't see in the physical dimension and still you can see the physical world around you. In this dimension you realize that the same old things that you lived with and thought to be the only facts in your physical reality look totally different; the walls of your room, the gravity, the speed of movement in the room or outside, your vision and other things. Yes, David you reach a purer dimension of the same reality.

"In the future, David, you will learn how to leave your soul body in the same way as you have left your physical body. You will then find yourself perceiving a higher dimension than the one you are now in. Until one day you will reach the dimension which only very few humans have ever perceived and participated in. So when you learn now about the different ten levels, I want you to pay attention and remember that they are all part of the same Universe—dimensions inside dimensions which coexist everywhere in the Universe, whether it is in your room or in a faraway galaxy. Each dimension actually occupies the entire Universe. Again, David, I want you to be aware that although I will talk about a purer dimension, or dimensions, that contains small particles compared to those which are composed of bigger ones, each dimension actually occupies the entire Universe. Yes, it is the description of the very same Universe, but each time from a different dimension, a different point of view. When you reach other dimensions you will notice that each has its own characteristics and is purer than the previous ones in terms of life forms and matter."

It sounded fascinating to me . . . I never thought there were other planes to be perceived beyond the amazing astral level . . . my place of adventures . . . I'm ready to listen. Maybe one day I will be able to visit one of the higher dimensions as Lamdiel mentioned now . . . I was excited and eager to learn more.

"One day." The angel smiled at me, reacting to my thoughts, and then continued. "David, before we start with the description of the levels, I want you to know that the names that we, the angels, or even the helpers, choose when communicating with the physical level, have no real value in any way, except to make the concepts that the names symbolize easier to remember. This also pertains to the names of the angels themselves and any other things in the Universe. Now open yourself, David, to absorb the information that will forever change your perspective of the whole Universe and the life in it. Let's start with the first dimension, the purest dimension of all, and then continue through all the other levels of the Universe. In the future you will learn in depth about each of these dimensions.

"The first dimension is called the infinite level. It is composed of the smallest, purest living units plus the smallest physical matters and nonphysical matters. These are the basics for all of the life forms in all of the ten dimensions. This is the level of the Creator who is the total sum of all the living units, the physical matter, the nonphysical matter and the entire space in the Universe, yes, David, including you and me."

Me . . . ? I don't feel a part of a big . . .

"Let me now give you an example because I know that you feel yourself to be a totally separate living creature from the Creator. Let's take, for example, your own body on the physical level. You perceive yourself as one complete unit which you call a human being. And you are right in thinking so. But inside of your body there are trillions of living cells; each one of which perceives its own life as a complete being, totally separated from the entire body, which is you. The cell may not be aware, but it must comply with the laws of Nature pertaining to its life structure as part of your body. This is similar to the rules needed for your own existence as a human being. If you want to see it even more deeply, that same cell is composed of smaller items such as proteins, molecules and atoms. Each one of these items is still part of your body; the same as you, I and even the Solar System or the galaxies are part of the Creator."

I looked at the angel, realizing how ignorant I had been so far.

The angel just smiled and continued.

"The second dimension is called the divine level. The most powerful angels and entities in the Universe are in this level. The big ones in this level are known as the Old Spirits and the Young Spirits. Their size is equivalent to the size of hundreds of clusters made out of thousands of galaxies. There are many thousands of spirits with this enormous size—both, from the Old Spirits and the Young Spirits. Each one of these groups can communicate directly with the Creator, and in this way, partially influence the laws of Nature and to some extent our destiny. Although I mentioned to you the big ones in this dimension, I want you to know that there are also smaller sized spirits in this level as well, actually in every dimension in the Universe. In the purer dimensions, the differences between the largest living spirits and the smallest ones are tremendously huge. In the less purer levels, such as on the physical one, the differences between the smallest and the biggest life forms are less prominent. For example, the size of a virus compared to an ancient dinosaur on your planet.

"The divine level can be perceived by angels of the third dimension and, of course, by the Creator who perceives all the other dimensions in the Universe.

"The third dimension is called the forces. Angels and other

big and powerful entities do exist in this level. The size of the biggest ones in this dimension is like a cluster of galaxies. Other spirits, ones who are much smaller, exist as well in this dimension. I and the angel Upiel exist normally in this dimension. In our level I look like the size of an entire planet, and the angel Upiel looks like the entire sun of your Solar System. We are not the biggest ones in our level, but our structure resembles that of human souls, therefore we are working with humans.

"When a spiritual being mentions 'Divine Forces' it pertains to the young spirits of the divine level and their assistants in the forces level. Together they are simply called 'DIVINE FORCES' who together with other lower levels, support the accelerated evolutionary doctrine, which is part of the Creator's will. The spirits in the force level are perceived by the spirits of the fourth dimension as you perceive the astral level."

"The fourth dimension is called the wise level. In this level other types of angels and entities live their lives. The big ones of this level are as a size of a whole star with its planets, similar to the sun and its planets and moons. So it is actually an enormous size for those angelic or spirit forms. Spirits in this level can be perceived by the spirits of the fifth dimension. Again, as you perceive the astral level.

"The fifth dimension is called the light level. In this dimension angels and entities exist as well. They sometimes communicate with selected individuals in the lower dimensions of the Universe, such as humans from the physical level. It is rare, but does happen, David. In this level there are many powerful entities who have helped during the centuries to facilitate the evolution of humanoids in the physical dimension of the Universe through selected helpers from that dimension. The biggest spirits in this level are about the size of an average planet in your galaxy. And as I mentioned to you regarding the other dimensions, there are many other very small spirits in this level as well. In the future we shall explore the light level dimension in depth. This will be your main level of spiritual activity.

"The sixth dimension is the eteric level. In this level exist spirits who usually do not communicate with the physical level. They have their own life activity. The biggest entities in this dimension are the size of a large mountain, but there exist many smaller entities as well. This is also the dimension where souls who leave the physical and astral levels, after completing their life cycles, are waiting in a semi-sleep state for their next reincarnation cycle. The waiting area at the eteric level is the place where all spirits of humanoids, animals, plants and even germs in the entire Universe wait for their reincarnation. Each one waits in the waiting area next to its planet. The same laws apply to all.

"The seventh dimension is the astral one. This is the place where you are now, David. This is the dimension in which the human's soul operates when attached to the body with what you perceived as a cord, whether you are in or out of your physical body. In this dimension all spirits of the animal and plant kingdoms operate as well. In the astral level live spirits who do not reincarnate into the physical body. They live their entire cycle in this level very much like humans live in the physical dimension.

"In the astral level you can find all the souls who, for some reasons, have refused to continue their reincarnation process after they passed away and left their physical body.

"These seven dimensions, as I told you, may be perceived in the physical level as nonphysical dimensions due to lack of appropriate awareness. This approach will change in the future when humanity on Earth will be ready to open up to the existence of higher perceptions.

"The eighth dimension is also called the physical level. This is where your physical body and all other humans on your planet and those on the many other planets in the Universe exist. Spirits from the astral level join the physical level to create the various life forms on your planet—humans, animals, plants and so forth. Spirits from the third dimension of the Universe—in certain conditions—join planets, and even some stars, and create huge life forms in the physical level.

"The ninth dimension, which is the cluster level, is also known as the supergalactic level. This dimension is huge, David. Just imagine that in the ninth dimension each star system, similar to your Solar System, is perceived as an atom, and each galaxy is perceived as a giant molecule, and a supercluster of galaxies is perceived as matter. There is life in this dimension as well. Spirits of the divine level join this dimension, creating huge life forms in the size of superclusters of galaxies.

"Last comes the tenth dimension which is the finite level, also known as the Universe level. This together with the first level, the infinite level—which is the purest base of all the other levels—creates the largest life form of all, the whole Universe which is actually the CREATOR."

"Wow!"

"Yes, David, the entire Universe, including space, is in reality one single life form—the Creator. The Creator contains all the life forms in the entire Universe, huge ones or miniature. Each has its roots in the infinite level, therefore we are all part of the Creator. But we are part of Him, similar to a single atom or a single living cell in your physical body is part of your conscious mind. It does not mean that the single atom or the single cell can communicate with you. It is the same as between you and the Creator. Even if, in theory, you could reach the infinite level, still the size of the Creator is the entire Universe. Therefore, you could not communicate directly with Him. The Creator is simply too big for you and with many trillions of trillions of things to focus upon; it is impossible for your size of living energy as a human being to communicate directly with Him. Some big entities can do it. As for us, the angels of the third dimension, in terms of energy intensity or size, we can communicate with those entities who can communicate with the Creator. In this indirect way we can have some type of communication with the Creator. But even for us, the angels, it is not something that we can do often.

"The life structure, as I described it to you, can be recognized mainly by those who live in purer dimensions and, of course, by those in the same level, but never by a lower level of existence. For example, a spirit within the eteric level can recognize life on the eteric, the astral and physical levels, but the spirit within the astral level cannot recognize the life forms within the eteric level or the purer levels.

"The infinite level, in which the foundations of the Creator exist, can recognize the living structures of all levels, understand their evolutionary needs, and then, with a special technique, communicate with all of them. The less purer levels cannot recognize or communicate with the infinite level, which is the purest, or if you want, the one which contains the smallest units in the Universe. It is so hard for most of the life forms, even for the very elevated ones, to know about, or communicate with the Creator who is the summation of the entire infinite level. Unless, for example, highly developed life forms of the divine dimension leave their level of existence and visit the infinite dimension. In that case some can only watch and others may communicate.

"In order for us, the angels of the third dimension, to reach the infinite level, we have to do it exactly as you do now, David, when visiting the astral world with your soul body, leaving your physical body to rest on your bed while you are here with me, right?" Smiled Lamdiel. "Can you understand so far, David?" The angel changed his voice, breaking the long speech.

I was fascinated, hypnotized by his musical, powerful and rich voice. There was no way I could think or look anywhere else because the voice was so magnetic, rapid and demanding at the same time. This fact together with the energy I had received in the beginning of the session made everything he said fully transmitted into my soul's mind. Yet I wasn't really sure that I had understood the meaning of everything. There was nothing concrete in the lecture, only theories of the Universe, but I felt that everything he said was in my memory.

"I do understand your lesson, but the reality is that I don't understand what you want to teach me in the practical aspects of my activity."

At that time I didn't care much about the structure of life or that of the Universe. I was more interested in adventures and excitement. Nevertheless, I wanted to have immediate response to the issues I encountered in the astral world rather than theoretical lectures.

The angel looked at me with a loving, understanding smile and then continued with the musical, rich voice, "Don't worry, David. Be patient and soon you will understand the structure of the Universe, the logic of life and many of your questions will be addressed.

"Now, David, go back to your body and be prepared to wake up in a few minutes for a night exercise. The military instructor of your class is planning it now for your entire class. I want to see you here at the same time tomorrow."

With this unexpected warning, I found myself back in my body, feeling super alert as if I had slept the whole night. I turned on my stomach and stared at the door. Then, as soon as I just began to think whether to start getting dressed or to wait, the instructor opened the door in a storm and turned on the lights, shouting, "Get up everyone! In three minutes you are outside, fully dressed, and ready to run the run of your life!"

I couldn't avoid smiling at him when my open eyes met his eyes. But my great feelings were somehow disturbed when the look on his face changed to an angry one. Probably I was too happy and too ready for the event. I must hide my feelings in the future . . . I concluded and immediately changed my facial expression to a more serious one.

Next morning I woke up feeling very energetic. The long running at night didn't leave me tired at all. I felt that the studying with the angel really reinforced me in all aspects. My thinking became sharper and little questions started to be solved, but there was still a lot to learn about this huge Universe in which I suddenly felt very small. All morning I found myself repeating the basics of yesterday's lecture, as if I were singing my favorite song, but this time the song was the musical voice of Lamdiel and its lesson; the ten levels of the Universe, the Creator, the angels and entities hierarchy. Yes, I was actually repeating all of the data about the fascinating world that had started to be revealed to me.

9
The Inner Reality of Matter—The Atoms and Their Subatoms

$\mathbb{T}$he night arrived, and I was again above the sea with the angel Lamdiel, waiting to explore more about this unknown Universe.

"Tonight, David, you will get answers to some of the main questions you raised when you started to explore the astral dimension by yourself: Why you can see or walk through walls, why you can reach enormous speeds which let you be in an instant anywhere you wish, and more. So be patient, and listen carefully. Try to visualize everything I tell you, and soon you will have some answers."

"Oh, thank you, Lamdiel." I was happy and excited, ready to absorb every word of his lecture.

"Let's focus, first, on the physical matter of the Universe. Did you ever wonder about the similarity between the atoms and your Solar System? They are similar, but also very different in properties. Therefore, Earth's scientists concluded that there is no similarity at all between the structure of the atom and that of the Solar System. The Solar System as well as any other star, the galaxies, the supergalaxies and the cluster of galaxies are all made from the same atoms of which your body is made.

"Now let's analyze the atom.

"This will surprise you, David. As you know from what you have learned in school, the atoms are the basic structure of the Solar System, of your body, and of everything you know around you. The atoms, as you have learned, are basically made of three main parts: the proton with positive electromagnetic charge, the neutron which is neutral with no apparent electromagnetic charge, and the electron which has the negative or the minus electromagnetic charge.

"Let's go behind the present discoveries of Earth science. The reality is that the atom is made from very small particles. There are eighty-eight different types of subatom 7. They are similar in structure to the atoms, but much smaller than the atom. In comparison, those units that we shall call subatoms, are in size parallel to the differences in size as the relationship of the entire Solar System to a single atom, let's say of hydrogen.

"Can you imagine such an unthinkably small size?

"In order for you to have an idea, just try to imagine to yourself the size of one atom. It is so small that you can put together many trillions of atoms in the length of one millimeter.

"The number of subatoms—called subatom 7—that you can put together in a linear line of one single atom is a number of many trillions subatoms. Actually there are: 1.7×10^{60} which is a number that starts with seventeen, and has fifty nine zeros following the seven, or sixty figures after the one: 1,700,000,000,000,000,000,000,000,000,000,000,000,000,000,000,000,000,000,000,000,000

"Just imagine how small is the size of the subatom 7. Later on, you will learn in more detail the properties of the subatoms and the importance of your understanding of this basic concept. The subatom 7's particles have similar bonds to each other, but with some definite different characteristics between them. In comparison, they are similar to the structure of the atoms, which can make some definite bonds in between themselves, in the various compounds described in chemistry.

"In reality, the subatom 7 creates an infinite quantity of different materials, part of them are liquids; others, gases; yet others, solid materials. When they are bonded together in very large numbers, they unite themselves in a unique form that you call an atom.

"In short, to repeat it differently: The atoms that you know are made from subatoms 7. There are eighty-eight different subatoms 7. Each one of the subatoms 7 has different characteristics. These are determined according to the energy surrounding their nuclei. This energy looks like a cloud of energy with very fast movement around the nucleus. According to the quantity of energy around the nucleus, it will determine the type of a specific subatom 7 out of the eighty-eight naturally occurring ones. Together they compose the basic structure of the particles of the atoms, the protons, neutrons, electrons, and even the photons—which are light particles—all are made of subatom 7.

"This natural phenomenon is, actually, similar to the way the atoms create the Solar System and the various materials in it.

"Another thing which will be interesting for you to know is that all atoms of the same category, such as for example, hydrogen, carbon, gold and others, are not the same. It really depends on the subatom 7 combinations that the atom is made from. Two atoms of the same category are never the same. Very much like two star systems with the same number of planets and the same star size and weight are never the same. They also depend on the atoms' configurations in them.

"David, it is something for you to think about because that is the main reason for so many changeable, stable and unstable, structures in the Universe.

"Now, let's go back to the astral level—the dimension in which your soul is right now. The people of Earth consider it, if at all accepting its existence, as a pure energy, but in reality the astral level is composed mainly from the subatoms 7's particles. They are so small that there is no way people on Earth can detect them today with their measuring instruments, which are made from such huge atoms in comparison to subatoms 7. Nor can they have a way to isolate them, simply because there is no way you can isolate such a small particle as the subatom 7 with any tool made out of atoms. It is similar, by comparison, to assume that a complex of galaxies can hold or isolate a single or a group of atoms.

"Your soul body in the astral level is, actually, a group of subatoms 7 in a very elastic, semiliquid form which is also a complex of many living units connected to the structure of the subatom 7 form. In a similar way, your soul is connected to your body.

"Let's answer your question of how can you pass through walls. Your astral body is so flexible and has such small units compared to the standard of the physical dimension matter that it can pass through any physical structure made of atoms with no restrictions at all.

"It is like passing with enormous speed through the galaxies with a small missile or spaceship. In a way, you can compare it to an X-ray which passes with ease through any given material which is less compressed than lead.

"Now you can understand, David, how you could pass so easily through walls or any type of material made of atoms. For you, in this level, it is simply passing through giant holes in the matter. Therefore, you can see through the walls as well.

"You wondered about the sources of the spectacular white cosmic light which you see as constant illumination in the astral level. You wanted to know why you could detect everything with ease.

"David, the answer is simple. Regardless of daytime or nighttime, matter in every level emits light or emits energy. Materials in every level of the Universe contain hidden energy which also has its own subatomic heat. Therefore they emit rays or waves of energy which the observer can consider as rays of light. In the astral level there are two main sources of light. Each planet in your Solar System, for example, is made of atoms which also radiate on their subatomic level, thus creating their own source of light for the viewer on the astral level.

"In addition to the first source of light, which is the various stars and planets, there are enormous groups of subatom 7 which are not condensed into the physical, atom level. These giant groups of subatom 7 look like enormous uncondensed clouds of matter present all over the Universe. In their size they are bigger than planets, and some of them are bigger than galaxies. Others are even bigger than superclusters. Each one of them is a source of light. The light which is emitted from the many subatom 7 sources all over the Universe crosses planet Earth and gives the spirits at the astral level a steady, constant light.

"On the subatom 7 level—the astral level—there is no heat such as that in an atomic reaction to create the phenomenon of light as is created by your sun, for example. The light extracted from the large subatom 7 starlike clouds emits, in reality, various degrees of light intensity. Because there are many clouds and planets of subatom 7 all around the astral dimension, the feeling of the observers is that the light in the astral level is equal everywhere they look, whether deep into the core of Earth, or throughout space, between galaxies. The light looks like a steady, clear, bright golden white light in all directions. Also, due to the enormous speed of light in the astral level, which is many trillions of times the speed of light within the physical level, the clarity of subjects is many millions times clearer than what you can perceive within the physical level of the Universe.

"The soul in the astral level has receptors which are sensitive to the astral light. Sometimes people can see the astral light while they are on the physical level due to one of many reasons such as while in a special meditation training, extreme tiredness and other situations which lower the activity of their cognitive mind.

"When you meditate or deeply relax, your mind is better

connected to your soul; you become more aware of your soul. Next, you can see the cosmic white light through the eyes of your soul. Even a blind individual can see the astral light from time to time in those situations. The light is usually seen through the outer angle of the eye, or even with closed eyes through that which is called the third eye."

"Blind people can see the cosmic light of subatom 7 when they are in their physical level!?" I became excited.

"Yes, David, there is a lot to learn about the physics and chemistry of the subatom 7 which is the basic foundation of the physical level of the Universe, but this is not all of the matter in the Universe. There are incredible, smaller particles which compose, or which are the foundations for, the astral level with its subatom 7.

"Each one of these levels that I've just mentioned to you today has a full structure, dynamics, and forces which are acting in their unique way. Yes, when you come to think about it, the Universe is a complex of different sizes fully composed of life and activities.

"Now, David, let me repeat it. We have been focusing ourselves, so far, on the matter of the seventh level—one which actually contains other subatomic levels. Subatom 7 is a small particle which is composed of much smaller particles. We can call them subatoms 6.

"Wow, it sounds like the explanation of dimensions inside dimensions." I tried to understand.

"That is right, David. The same as that many subatom 7 compose the atom of the physical level, many subatom 6 compose each subatom 7 of the astral level.

"Each subatom 7 contains sixty-nine types of naturally occurring subatoms 6. Their structure is similar to that of subatom 7, but with some differences. They also emit a type of radiation, stronger than the subatom 7. Their radiation can be detected within the eteric level or purer levels, but not from the astral nor the physical one. Therefore, once you will have learned how to leave your astral body and to go into the eteric level of existence, you will be pleasantly surprised at how much better your vision is. Also, since the speed of the particles on each purer level is tremendously faster than the previous one, you will notice, then, that your personal speed, reaction, thinking and even learning is going to be considerably faster than the one you are now in.

"David, the story does not end here. There are more levels of existence as you already know, and each one of them has its own subatomic structure. Therefore, you can imagine by now that the subatom 6 is made from even smaller particles. They are called the subatom 5 which again is the foundation for the subatom 6. We call them in a simple way for you to remember them and their hierarchy by numbers, but don't worry if you aren't yet acquainted with them. In the future you will learn much more in detail about the structure, bonds, composition and characteristics of each level, together with their subatomic foundation.

"Now, in order for us to continue, all you have to remember is that the dimensions of the Universe are composed all the way down from quite infinite sizes of subatoms. I know that for you, right now, it is impossible to grasp the infinite size of a single atom, not to mention its known particles accepted by science people on Earth.

"I know it is even harder to imagine the subatom 7 and then the subatom 6 and the subatom 5, but the structure of the Universe simply does not end here, so be more patient, and we shall cover briefly the entire structure, OK, David?"

I wasn't really reacting. I could accept his words in theory, but when I was really trying to imagine the infinite small sizes of the particles, it was virtually impossible for me to do so.

Then the angel continued a little bit faster, as if to indicate to me that it was only general knowledge. For me it was clear that I would learn it in detail at some time in the future.

"Let's continue with the basic structure of each dimension,

each level of existence. The subatom 5 is made similarly from subatom 4. The subatom 4 is made similarly from subatom 3. The subatom 3 is made similarly from subatom 2, and the subatom 2 is made similarly from subatom 1, which is the foundation for all, including each and every material in the Universe. This is the smallest matter that appears in the infinite level.

"Actually, the structure of the Universe is much more complex because, in addition to the seven different levels of subatoms, there are other types of particles that are 'visiting' our Universe from other Universes, each with different structures and properties. We will not discuss this now.

It astonished me. "I . . . didn't know that there are other Universes." I exclaimed, feeling overwhelmed.

"Yes, David, but let's focus on our Universe and let's review it again from another perspective.

"Each level of subatom, in comparison to a preceding, less purer level of subatom, is so small, exactly like the atom is in comparison to the Solar System. This structure is sized down all the way to subatom 1 in the infinite level. The subatom 1 is the smallest, purest matter in the Universe. It is almost considered by us as nonexistent, but this miniature size should not mislead you. It is actually—together with pure living units and energy—the base of all compounded life forms, from the simplest life forms to the most complex life form in the Universe, which we call the tenth level—the finite level, which is the Creator. In this way, the first level, the infinite, is the base for all the levels in the Universe, including the tenth level.

"David, simply you should remember that all the levels are one compounded Universe.

"In our very primary life origin, we are all made from subatom 1, living units and energy. These also compose the Creator structure.

"The subatom 1 has totally different characteristics from the other ones. It looks more like a miniature energy unit, with nearly infinite velocity, many trillions of trillions of times the speed of the physical level's light, which you ironically consider on Earth, so far, as the accepted maximum speed possible in the whole Universe.

"David, although I touched this concept of the subatoms very briefly now, I know that it is a complicated concept for you. Maybe, at present, you can accept it theoretically, but it is hard to imagine such a small almost nonexistent particle. Yet, in spite of its infinite miniature size, it connects with living units, and therefore, it has the eternal wisdom of the creation with feelings and recognition of the self, and all of the other characteristics of life that you shall learn about later.

"Now let's continue a little bit further. Earth scientists believe, as I told you earlier, that the ultimate velocity in the Universe is the speed of light. They were right, but only to a degree, which is for describing the properties of the atom in the physical level. But, when we are dealing with a much purer material such as the subatom 7 at the astral level, the laws of Nature are different from the ones you know so far in the observable reality from Earth.

"One of the main differences is the speed. The subatom 7 level, which we can call also the astral level of existence, has its own maximum speed of astral light. It also has its own light wave that is actually emitted or created from the constant exchange of particles in the astral level. This light has a speed which is much faster than the 'speed of light.' It means that the spirit within the astral level has a speed which is much faster than the speed of light. It is actually the speed of many, many millions of miles per second. The light on the astral level has a constant speed, or calculated in kilometers per second, about 6×10^{36} kilometers per second, which is a huge number of six with thirty-six zeros after the six :

6,000,000,000,000,000,000,000,000,000,000,000,000 kilometers per second. Compare this number to the physical speed of light which is approximately 300,000 kilometers per second—can you see the difference, David?

"Yes," I answered. I was excited about the new knowledge.

"David, this huge number, six followed by thirty six zeroes is nearly the constant light speed in the astral world. The soul at his maximum speed travels in the vicinity of less than one millionth of that speed. This is an enormous speed compared to the speed people, or even the fastest missile, can move. That is the reason why the soul at the astral level feels that he can reach anywhere he wishes to be in a split second.

"The soul is made of a very tiny particle compared to Earth, and the atomic structure of the physical level creates a closed cycle which does not affect the astral level. Therefore, there is no gravity effect on the soul at the astral level. And this is why a soul can float everywhere he wants. The main force to move the soul is his own will which in a subconscious way creates a type of energy bond to the place, or person, to which the soul wants to go. This magnetic, telepathic bond moves the soul almost immediately to the place the soul wants to be, and this is the real mechanism that enables the soul to travel in the astral dimension.

"Now with each purer or more elevated level of existence, the speed is considerably faster. The reactions and ability to move are much faster than the previous one. Also, the ability to absorb knowledge and understanding is much wider.

"Another phenomenon that you will notice in the future is that the spirits who live in the purer levels have a bigger and stronger energy compared to the previous level. In other words, the purer the spirit, the stronger he is. This phenomenon continues all the way to the purer level, until reaching the ultimate in speed, size, power, wisdom and the many other qualities that the Creator has in infinite amounts."

The angel paused for a moment, and then, in different voice, said, "You can go back to your body and have some sleep now, David. I will see you here tomorrow night."

In a split second I was back in my bed and soon I fell into a deep pleasant sleep until the morning.

10
Feeling Different

The next day I could not stop thinking about those numbers which were representing very small, infinite parts of the millimeter. Those numbers were so miniature that I could only repeat and understand the numbers, but not visualize their real size. It was all a new concept for me. I was trying with all my heart to grasp the structure of the Universe. Amazingly, I felt as if I were listening to an audiotape within myself. I was simply digesting the information in such an accurate way as had never happened to me before. I never had believed that I would have such a great memory. Maybe I remembered so clearly everything the angel had said just because it had been such different information from what I had gotten in my regular studies at the boarding school. The angel had really given me a very different outlook and understanding of the Universe.

While trying to analyze my reasons for repeating the angel's lecture by heart, something in me, an inner voice, didn't agree with me, "You are wrong, David, that isn't the reason. You know the lecture by heart because the angel's information entered directly into the memory storage of your soul . . . "

Shortly after, the daily routine at school took over my time and attention to such a degree that I almost forgot about the night's teachings.

The evening eventually arrived and soon I was again above the Mediterranean Sea. Lamdiel was already there, radiating an enormous inner light as I appeared in front of him. With his unique, rich voice he continued to teach me about the Universe and the life in it. I kept meeting with him every night at the same time at the same place above the sea. His lectures were all fascinating to me. I never in my life had thought I would come across such information about what I used to call simply the Universe.

Two weeks passed by, and I was on my way home for a weekend vacation. Sitting in one of the last back seats in the bus that traveled toward the city of Tel Aviv, I constantly stared through the window, wondering about our Universe. Now with the vast information that had filled my head in the last two weeks, I began to observe everything around me with different eyes. I was excited, but kept reminding myself that it was only the beginning of the knowledge that I was going to receive from the angel and other entities. But even now, the Universe's reality already looked so different from the one that my father or my science teachers had been discussing. The new concepts were so wide, so endless. I just couldn't understand how it was possible that my father and the many well-educated scientists, having the best knowledge in the world, had no idea about the real Universe. Is it possible that they are so ignorant about the reality, exactly as we view today the scientific knowledge of two thousand years ago . . . ? Is it possible that once the knowledge of the real Universe, as explained by the angel, will be revealed, the present scientific knowledge will be considered a primitive one .. . ? Should I tell my father the new scientific information? This way he will not waste his precious time on misleading or even wrong scientific data which he and his colleague scientists had used for their endless researches . . .Yes, I must tell him . . . he is my father . . . I can't leave him in the dark . . . it can help him in his work . . . but I promised Upiel that I would keep everything secret . . . and besides Dad won't believe me . . . probably he will worry about my vivid imagination . . .

I tried to imagine to myself what would be my father's reaction if I told him even just a little of the information I had received from Lamdiel. Soon I remembered many of the talks we had had about the scientific researches and validation of scientific data. I could imagine his blue, smart eyes looking at me for a moment and then saying in his deep voice: "David, you need to be careful about accepting any new information or data as valid. If we accept anything we hear or read as if it were valid scientific data, then science wouldn't be science anymore. Science then would be full of imaginary and misleading facts. In the long run, they would block our ability to advance in real knowledge as it happened so clearly in the medieval times. Then science would be full of ghosts, spirits, fairy tales, legends and other false beliefs such as the assumption that Earth is the center of the Universe and the whole Universe moves around the Earth. And as it happened in the past, unproved data might lead the clear, precise scientific knowledge into many false and misleading concepts, which we, the scientists, during the last centuries have worked so hard to get rid of. And again, David, a true knowledge of the entire Universe is very hard to get. There are many assumptions and hypotheses as to the age, size, origin, forces and contents of the whole Universe and its segments. In order for us to accept any theory, we must challenge its logic and validate it in its various aspects. Only those aspects of information which successfully pass the test of challenging and which are confirmed as valid can be candidates for being accepted as part of the scientific reality. Not before that. And, David, no exceptions." I kept imagining my father talking to me while trying to conceal his shock after hearing my "new scientific data."

Then, remembering the conversations we had had in the previous years about researching the validity of the spiritual world, it was made clear to me that there was no chance that he would ever accept the angel's information as valid. He would never believe in angelic existence in the first place.

Eventually, the bus arrived at the Central Bus Station. Soon I was on the second bus that would take me home.

After 25 minutes I started to recognize the city. The idea of talking with my father about my new learning filled my head again.

I found myself in a real conflict. On one hand, I did agree that I had to keep the whole spiritual training confidential. But on the other hand, my loyalty to my family and, especially, to my father, made me feel that it was unfair to keep this enormous knowledge to myself without telling it to him. After all, he has been struggling all his life to find something new, a new discovery in science . . . Now that I had acquired so much new data from the spiritual world, it may help my father tremendously in his researches . . . but would he accept this knowledge . . . ? Wouldn't he take it as my own imagination and simply smile, ignoring it completely, or give me a moral lecture on science . . . ? I knew very deeply in my heart that this was exactly what he would do, but I couldn't avoid thinking about it. Suppose I decide to tell him all of what I know so far . . . but what proof do I have about the information that the angel gave me . . . ? How can I come to my father and tell him about angels, about speeds much faster than that of light, particles much smaller than the electron or photon, the ten levels of the Universe, and the existence of subatom 1 through subatom 7? How can I tell him that there is life after death, about living units—a force which is unknown yet to science, but nevertheless appears in all matter in the Universe . . . and that is why science was able to create life in the laboratory . . . ? How can I tell him that the origin of the Universe didn't and never did originate in the Big Bang . . . ? I can't even explain to him the similarity between the Solar System and the atom, after he explained to me a little while ago that this assumption had been the initial belief of the scientists when they first had discovered the structure of the atom . . . but then they had completely dropped this assumption, simply because the electron does not behave as a planet would behave, and there were other irregularities and differences which counteracted the similarities between the atomic structure and that of the Solar System. How can I tell him now that the initial assumptions were more valid than the current theories which the best scientists in the world believe in today . . . ?

I kept speculating for a while until all of a sudden I noticed that I was repeating the last two weeks lectures of the angel. It wasn't even difficult. I realized that his lectures were engraved in me, even those parts that at the time of the session seemed too difficult or technical. I remembered them word by word, number by number. I was amazed, simply amazed. Then I understood why, at the end of the second lecture, when I had asked Lamdiel whether I should write down everything when I went back to my physical body, he just had smiled and said, "Don't worry about it, David."

Soon the bus stopped at the station near my home, and my weekend vacation began. It was almost noon. My father came early from work that day as he usually did when he knew I would be home on vacation. We ate lunch and had a few talks about life while we played Chess together. I never mentioned a word about the new, endless Universe I had gotten to know, although I felt such an urge to do so every time he mentioned some of the latest research in physics. My mother came later in the afternoon so I spent some time with her as well.

That evening I met with my girlfriend, Josephine. We went to a movie and had a great time together. Then late at night, as soon as I returned to my parents' house, I went right to bed and started with the meditation to get out of my body again. I knew that Lamdiel would be waiting for me above the Mediterranean Sea. And he was.

As I came closer, he was there smiling at me with love. Then, as if he had followed me all day, he said, "David, we know how much you want to share the information that you have received from us. We know how lonely and different you feel at certain moments. But it is not the right time. There is still lots for you to learn. One day, when the time is right, you may share this knowledge with others."

I was too shaky to answer. Everything looked suddenly too overwhelming to me. But the radiation of loving energy from the angel dissolved all of my fears and excitement, leaving me fully relaxed as I absorbed his lecture.

The weekend passed by quickly and soon I was traveling back to the Central Bus Station. Sitting on the bus, I saw many girls who were going to school that morning. One of them resembled Josephine and that immediately filled me with some sadness. I missed Josephine and imagined I could take her to school with me, maybe hide her in my room during the days and then join her later in the evening secretly.

"Last stop!" the driver announced. I found myself in the Central Bus Station. The place was busy with people. They all walked fast, and seemed to hurry, maybe on their way to their work places or schools. I also walked fast so as not to miss the 7:00 a.m. bus which traveled up north.

Soon I was sitting by a slightly open window on one of the back seats of the bus. As we left the city, fresh air entered through it. I took a few deep breaths, enjoying the smell of the wild spring flowers which were blooming in their beautiful colors alongside the highway. Observing them, I felt so peaceful. There was more than half an hour to travel, so I decided to close my eyes and take a short nap.

As soon as I intended to do so, I suddenly had a strange feeling . . . I will not make it on time if I continue on this bus . . . why . . . ? I looked around. The bus was full of people; some of them were sitting, the others standing. They all looked serious, ready for a new full week of work or maybe of learning. The strange sensation was still there in my mind. I tried to brush it aside, but with every station where the bus stopped and every mile that it traveled, the sensation grew stronger. Then altogether it became so intense that I decided to take my backpack and get down at the next stop. And that was exactly what I did.

Sitting on the bench waiting for the next bus that was to go north, I felt a kind of relief. Beyond any logic, I knew, some-how, that I had made the right decision. Fifteen minutes later, I was on the next bus that headed north. It was also full of people. This time I had to stand, but I didn't really care. I just stared through the window, thinking about my astronomy teacher. Then, as soon as the bus was closer to the next stop, I noticed that the other bus—the one that I had traveled in—was off the road in an odd position. How strange . . . sensa-tions, coincidences . . . little miracles . . . in one's life . . . and they don't happen only to me, but to many other people I have known . . . Who is standing behind them . . . ? Why do some people have them more often than others . . . ? I hope the angel will teach me also about miracles and coincidences . . . I know he will, but when . . . ?

Soon I was at school. I somehow made it in at the last minute for breakfast and attended the first class on time. Ev-eryone seemed to be a little tired, probably from a busy week-end. Eventually the day passed by and lights-off time arrived. The air felt so pleasant that my roommates and I decided to leave the window open. Lying on my bed, I watched the full moon shining its light through the white transparent curtain which by now was moving with the gentle breeze from the sea.

"G h o s t s . . ." Aaron whispered from his bed.

"Yeah, sure. I can see one," Tom added and everyone laughed like crazy. I laughed, too . . . If they only knew what I do experience every night . . . what type of spirits really exist in the floating side . . .

But then I covered myself with the blanket and stared at

the ceiling. I felt lonely, in a funny way. It only showed me how far I had become apart from my classmates and their simple reality. Yes, although I was a welcome friend to most of my classmates, the other part in me made it clear that because of my new spiritual training and experiences, I felt an outsider in the boarding school . . . maybe an outsider in most other places as well . . .

It felt worse when I sensed this emotional emptiness and the shallow view of reality, not only in my classmates but also in my teachers and the other adults around me. I had become a different person from my classmates and friends. Thinking about it made me sad. What if I grow so different that I won't have any friends when I grow up . . . ? It was a scary thought and another thing to worry about. Would I find a loving girl-friend who will accept me as I am . . . ? Or maybe, with more spiritual education, I will be even more an outsider to the nor-mal daily reality, and then what will be my destiny . . . ? Should I hide myself from others for the rest of my life, even from my future wife and children . . . ? These are thoughts and ques-tions that I will have to ask the angel about . . . but maybe I should hide it from the angel as well because, if I'm in doubt, he might refuse to teach me further . . .

I was confused, but since I was committed anyway, I de-cided to focus on the positive part of my training in the astral world—the great place to be and to learn about life—hoping deep in my heart that my spiritual development would be a proper compensation for the loneliness which I was experienc-ing more and more every day.

Soon I began to think about my friend Ahmed. I had not seen him for a while. Although the angel Lamdiel, and earlier Upiel, were teaching me, it simply was not enough. I wanted to speak with a real person who was like me, but more experi-enced, someone whom I could learn from, and Ahmed was the perfect figure for that purpose. He was the only one of the helpers I had known who also had lived in Israel. The other helper whom I had gotten to know was Rabbi Joseph from Brooklyn, New York. He used to travel from the USA to Israel in his out-of-body state. According to what he had told me, it took him only a split second to get here. I liked him, but we didn't talk much. He always seemed to be busy helping some people who needed him.

Now, after the few sessions with Lamdiel, I knew for sure that simply to be in the astral reality was not enough—no matter how often I had visited there. I now realized that there was a lot to learn from the angel and, if I could, also from Ahmed. Thinking about the lectures with Lamdiel, I had no doubt that I was entering a new world of knowledge. It was one that not many people in the world would ever believe that it exists. I'm not alone . . . I belong now to a unique, small group of great people . . . the spiritual helpers who have been personally trained by the angels . . . They have the knowledge that I'm going to have . . .

This thought helped me to feel more secure and calm. I couldn't wait for the coming lessons with the angel Lamdiel.

* * *

The ten levels of the Universe are not real
levels that you reach as you climb higher.
These levels are the dimensions which coexist
in the same reality and place in the entire
Universe for as long as the Universe exists.

* * *

Each dimension actually occupies the entire
Universe. Yes, it is the description of the very
same Universe, but each time from a different
point of view.

* * *

11
The Soul—Bonding, Possession, and Depossession

The time to meet with the angel Lamdiel arrived again. And soon I was in front of him, feeling the radiation of light entering my whole soul.

"David, you remember the many questions you have had, and your constant feeling that there was no one to ask? Well, today we are going to cover another part of those questions. Yes, David, at some time in the future, after your initial spiritual training, you will learn how to reach into the light level of existence. It will happen to you as a part of your advanced spiritual training after you will establish the spiritual channels of communication while being in the astral level. By then most of your questions will be solved.

"Now, David, one of the first questions you wanted an answer for—remember as a child?—was 'What is the purpose of life? Why was I born?'

"There is an answer behind the obvious ones that 'your parents made you', or 'this is the mystery of Nature, life and evolution' or 'this is the will of God.'

"As you already have noticed, life is a universal phenomenon. There is life on all ten levels of the Universe—each with its own momentum and power. In humans, for example, the entrance of the soul into the fetus's body starts one of the many life cycles of that soul. But, in order for this bond of body and soul to happen, it requires a combination of matching qualities, goodwill, trust and acceptance of the soul by the fetus body for the coming life as the destiny of one's life in that specific cycle. These requirements usually come together with the instinct implanted in each and every soul—that is, the need for a complete investment in one's future. A life cycle or reincarnation is a step, a fraction, of the entire universal life cycle which every life form participates in. It is, David, a part of a long evolutionary process which eventually will unify all life forms in all of the dimensions with the Creator. All of the spirits in the Universe are aware of that fact. It is placed in their core awareness—this basic knowledge is maintained deep in the pure living units of the infinite level.

"David, you already know that life does not start when you are born nor finish when you are dead. Your time in the physical body is but a fraction of your total time alive. We are all part of the same creation or the Creator. Therefore, in the core of our souls, we are all living forever. The real question is, or should be, not if we shall live forever, but the QUALITY of life that we are going to have now and in the future. Are we improving our quality of life? Or are we destroying and worsening our present or future quality of life? Are we progressing in our evolutionary process?

"This should be the main concern of any life form. The obvious initial factors which can determine the quality of life for the newborn or the future generation of any particular life form, whether it is a microorganism, plant, animal or human, depend on various issues such as location, parents, particular code of genetic information and, to a degree, the parents' lifestyle and their ability to support their newborn.

"These factors are only a part of the many conditions that can affect the newborn. One's life quality and evolutionary process also depend on the cosmic-eco-system-balance conditions. The evolutionary process in humans and in the more elevated life forms depends on each individual, his investment in the positive evolution of one's life and one's group evolution. Next, the individual's evolutionary process depends on the entire race; then it goes as follows: on the entire living system on the planet on which he lives; on the Solar System to which one belongs; on the galaxy; on the supergalaxy, then on the super-cluster, and ultimately, in the long run, on the entire Universe—the Creator—who is the sum of the entire Universe with its laws of Nature that affect each and every one of the life forms in the Universe . . ."

My personal evolution depends on so many aspects . . . the galaxy, the whole Universe . . . ? That was too abstract for me and too big to relate to.

"You will learn more about it in the future, so even if it is not clear to you now, it will be, David." The angel smiled at me, responding to my thoughts.

"Life, in reality, is a gradual complex in which each particle in the Universe depends upon its surroundings. This reality actually goes all the way up to the entire Universe. The real cosmic-eco-system-balance, which every life form depends upon, is actually THE BALANCE SYSTEM OF THE ENTIRE UNIVERSE.

"You must remember this fact, because you will not learn it at your school. Science on Earth acknowledges mainly the effects of the planetary eco-system-balance on your life up to the level of the Solar System while, in reality, it is a much wider system than that. The more you will know about life in the Universe, the more you will understand that everything on all levels of existence depends on the whole and, at the same time, supports the whole. We can also name this phenomenon as 'the universal-eco-system-balance.'

" The universal-eco-system-balance affects the evolution of each one of you, including the reincarnation process which creates the future generations.

"The need to create a future generation in order to ensure the continuation of that specific race is implanted in every living organism as one of the main needs of any mature living creature in the Universe. But, what soul is going to enter and become part of such offspring?

"Let's take, for example, humans. The parents are not aware of it and they cannot decide or choose a soul for their newborn. But, indirectly, they can affect the conditions for a specific intensity of a soul to enter into the new fetus simply by the lifestyle they have had during their lives. This includes the type of emotional and spiritual aspects of their lives, health conditions and the many other aspects which can indirectly affect the process. Other than that, it is simply not up to them."

The angel paused for a moment, letting me absorb the lecture so far.

I was curious now. "But can the new soul decide about his reincarnation fate? Did I choose my parents?"

"Well, David, the answer is yes and no. The answer is compounded, because the waiting for reincarnation soul of a human or any other advanced life form, can, in theory, refuse to reincarnate in any given situation. There is a free will in the Universe. In order to avoid a specific destiny or cycle in the physical life, a soul may refuse, for example, to enter into a fetus who has a damaged body, or one who has a problematic pair of parents. But unless that soul decides to stay forever in the waiting area—which actually never happens—one cannot escape his own fate by that decision. The intensity of the soul's energy will allow him to enter into a specific reincarnation with a specific life cycle which is the optimum for that spirit. If he refuses to enter into a specific body in a specific reincarnation, he loses some additional small amount of energy which will eventually cause him to lose living units from the soul; thus, lowering the total intensity of his soul's energy. This means that the second opportunity would be even worse than the first one. On the subconscious level of the soul, each one is aware of this fact and therefore chooses to enter the reincarnation upon first opportunity. Also, the wish to be involved in the physical life governs the fears. Therefore, practically, the answer whether the soul can decide on any specific reincarnation or not will be NO.

"Another reason for the soul's inability to choose his own fate is that, in reality, the soul is waiting in a semi-sleep state of awareness at the waiting area of the eteric level. The waiting soul has neither the time nor awareness of the consequences for entering again into the new body. The reality of the reincarnation process goes very much in a semiautomatic channel with no real decision on the part of the waiting soul. Therefore, again, the answer will be, in practice, NO. The soul cannot choose his new reincarnation. In reality, you simply accepted to be born to your present parents—you did not choose them."

"What makes one soul have a better reincarnation or vice versa?" I was curious to know.

"It is a process which is determined mainly by the soul's previous life in the physical dimension and afterlife there—after the soul departs from the physical body. The more balanced and positive the previous life was, the more that particular soul gains intensity of energy which allows new living units to join that soul; therefore, he grows and, eventually, enters a better new reincarnation. On the other hand, if that person was acting in a negative way, opposing the needs or development of himself and/or his own race, species, and acting against other laws of Nature, then that specific soul loses energy. This practically means that some of the soul's newly joined living units depart from that soul, therefore leaving him with less intensity in terms of energy. As a result that soul, when the time is right, enters a less fortunate new life cycle that matches the present intensity of his soul.

"This chain of events which I just described to you, David, is only part of the whole process. The reincarnation process, including the quality of life and the partial ability to determine one's life as part of the big evolutionary cycle, is one of the main aspects that influence the long chain of events in life. You may call it: destiny, karma, fate, or gorral [Hebrew]. Whether we like it or not, it applies to all living things in the Universe.

You will learn more about it in the coming lessons.

"Now let's go back to the reincarnating soul. An 'Opening', or a 'vacuum-like' state, is being created by the new life or new fetus. It is actually created by a group of rapidly growing numbers of new living cells. These cells have a genetic imprinted wish to become united and physically bonded to each other. Nevertheless, they have also a real spiritual emptiness as part of their emotions. It is imprinted in their souls made of pure living units. The cells are seeking to fill this emptiness. They are actually anxious for a higher state of life through a very specific bond with a much bigger soul, one with a much higher intensity than their own souls. This is the routine way for faster evolution in the Universe. That bigger soul will enable them to grow and improve the quality of their life on a much higher level than they ever could accomplish by themselves. For the new mass of cells, it is the only condition in which they can continue and survive in that new form. As soon as the soul enters the body, a bonding process between the souls of the cells and that of the bigger soul begins. The new joining soul becomes responsible for their welfare. He has now to fulfill the various needs of the growing body. He also has to process the many different issues arising from conflicts of interest, different needs and emotions—the issues of the many trillions of living cells, each of which is a separate entity with its own needs and wishes. The new soul has a lot to do in terms of bonding, balancing and harmonizing the new group of cells into one well-synchronized, new, life form.

"This process happens the same in plants, animals, or humans. When you come to think about this kind of evolution—it is a truly synergic process. The new bonded whole colony of cells into a new higher life form is much more capable of reaching higher levels of life than each of its living cell units individually."

I was amazed. I never had thought about the little cells of my body as little entities who have their own lives, wishes and emotions. Now we are one. But how do they bond to my soul . . . ? Can another soul enter into my body besides the one that reincarnates into it . . . ?

The angel smiled at me. "David, you were not the only one, but most humans on Earth are unaware of the living souls in each one of the cells. Being aware of them can help solve many of the health problems on Earth. Yes, David, the bonding of the soul with the body is a serious topic. When we focus on the various healing processes, this topic will be discussed. At that time we shall cover in depth more aspects of this natural phenomenon and its relationship to the human's health, and how it affects the body and character of people. You will also learn how parents can help their future newborn to have a better soul entering into him or her.

"Now, for the bonding of the cells' souls and the reincarnated soul. This bonding is not done in one day. It is a process which has six stages in the life of humans. Another soul or a possession of a spirit into the body of an animal or a person is possible when the mechanism of the bonding is, for some reason, imperfect. This allows different levels of interaction between an intruder's spirit and the body cells. The majority of the cases, over 99.99 percent of all attempts by spirits to possess bodies, are the souls of humans who, for any reason, have refused to continue the reincarnation process, and, after a while, they feel the urge to manifest themselves. Obviously they try to enter where they feel it is safe for them to do so."

With these words, the angel stopped his lecture and sent me down to my physical body.

Next morning I felt great. My energy level was high all day. Swimming the weekly swim of three miles in the sea, I somehow reached the other side of the pier faster than ever before, leaving most of my classmates behind.

Soon the evening arrived and there I was again above the sea ready for my next lesson.

"David, I'm going to tell you briefly about the six stages of the soul's bonding process with the body cells, and mention the issue of possession. Later you will learn all about the mechanism of possession and how to depossess an intruding spirit from a hosting body.

"There is no fixed time for the souls to enter into the new body. We can look at it this way: As soon as the new, rapidly growing cells in the fetus reach some accepted form, the mini-souls of the most developed cells, which are the cells of the nervous system, start intuitively to look for their stabilizer in life, their source for meaningful life, which is the bonding with a much stronger soul. One who will bring a better life into their, otherwise, simple existence. At this time, the cells' souls become united and do cooperate within their level of awareness and create a special energy vacuum. This sends a clear signal with a specific intensity of energy which awakens the waiting soul—one who has the exact, matching level of energy intensity that will fit into that body and that life cycle. This is actually the summation of the total quantity of living units within the reincarnating soul. That soul, then, has the opportunity to enter into the new body—to reincarnate into a new life cycle. And for you humans, you may consider this moment as the real time that a new life begins. In humans it begins between three to four weeks and up to about six weeks after the fertilization takes place. Sometimes it takes even a longer period of time after conception for the new soul to join the newly forming body. On his way to the physical body, the soul passes through the astral level and assumes automatically a new astral body.

"In the first stage, the soul enters into the new body of the fetus. From the soul's point of view, he just has awakened with a need to enter into a new life. At that moment the soul is not fully aware of what is going to happen, but usually, no matter how hard or how negative the coming incarnation is going to be, the soul accepts it, mainly ignoring his own ability to perceive his future. It is like being very hungry, then eating while ignoring the ingredients of the main dish; you can inform yourself about the food you eat, but you may not really care. The same with the soul. He is in a semi-sleep state, but at the same time has the craving to be back into the action that the physical dimension offers. In a remote part of the soul's mind, he knows that the coming events are in a perfect match with his destiny, so there is no reason to refuse the coming reincarnation, no matter how good or bad it is going to be.

"Again, David, the soul might refuse to reincarnate into a specific fetus, but in practice it almost never happens. In the few cases when it does happen, it is usually due to the soul's own traumas, fears and damages which make that soul unready for any future incarnation. It is not because of refusing that specific fetus's destiny.

"Let's explore, now, the first stage from the fetus's body's point of view. In reality, it is a type of marriage between the body and the soul. In this case, the body feels the need to grow by bonding with a bigger and stronger soul. As I mentioned to you, the information is implanted in the awareness of the pure living units in the little souls of the body cells. The soul connects himself initially with the more reactive cells of the new body which are usually those of the nervous system in animals and humans. Not all cells in the body have the same intensity of soul. The most primitive ones are the storage cells, which are the souls of the adipose—the fatty cells. They have low intensity souls. The most advanced ones, the nerve cells—the neurons—have different levels of intensity according to the position they are going to take in the life of that person. Those who are awakened into the need of integration with a bigger soul are the cells' souls of the nervous system located in the brain and especially those of the brain core, in both hemispheres of the brain. It usually happens in the human race of today at the very early stages when the cells of the fetus become aware of their future needs to cooperate with a much bigger soul than themselves.

"The time sequence depends on many factors, including the cells' conditions, the soul's readiness to evolve, the condition of the carrier mother, the genetic factors of the cells and many more issues.

"The order in which the soul becomes attached to the body cells is very important when we need to address the possibility of various traumatic events in the healing process, but don't be concerned about that now. We shall learn about them in the future.

"In the initial steps of the bonding process, the human soul enters into the body, adjusting his energy intensity to the fetus's size, and starts the bonding of the soul with the souls of a few nerve cells in the brain. Most of the soul's awareness at this stage is focused on the new environment, occupying every new nerve cell that it can. The cells' souls, seeking the unification with the much bigger soul, are ready and willing to be united. Therefore, it is a simple process in spite of the initial shock for both, for the soul to awaken into a complete new reality, and the cells' souls who are so busy to complete the enormous physical and mental growth demanded by the genetic code of their cells and the codes imprinted in the pure living units in their own souls. As in any new beginning, demands and lifestyle, there are some trials and errors which can occur in every stage of life and, accordingly, problems may arise and also be solved.

"By learning about the bonding or adaptation process, you will be able to see how and when possessing spirits may penetrate a person's body. At this time, no possession by other spirits can occur. First, because there is no space left over for another spirit and, secondly, as strange as it sounds to you, the mother's soul becomes very much protective and involved in the fetus's life. This is done on higher levels of awareness and would normally protect the new fetus from any potential spirit intruder even if the mother is not consciously aware of this phenomenon.

"Even in cases when the mother is against the birth of a new baby, or consciously plans to have an abortion, that fetus is protected by the mother's soul for as long as he is nurtured by the mother. There are many factors that might affect the bonding period besides those of the soul's activities. These factors are important. They include the physical and mental state of the carrier who is normally the biological mother.

"Again, David, don't worry if the whole picture is unclear right now. When we will teach you about health and healing, then we shall address the soul's bonding with the body in much more detail.

"The soul, by now, lives in the new reality and, gradually is forgetting his previous life, or is actually storing his previous life into his soul's memory bank, usually in the eteric level of the soul. At that time he is removing the previous life information from the soul's conscious awareness. Sometimes when the soul refuses to forget the previous identity, there is a natural process of forgetfulness—one which might be longer than usual and may extend even after birth.

"Remembering the previous life, or lives, is not beneficial to the newborn. Therefore, it is rare to find a young child who lives in the memories of a past life. Some remote or partial memories might emerge from the soul's memory bank. Nevertheless, they usually are of such low intensity that they will not disturb the present life.

"Among humans, at some places on Earth, people of a specific group or culture accept the reincarnation process as a factual, natural process and, therefore, make the memories of a past life for young children a positive and rewarding experience. Some children of these cultures might partially recall their previous lives or specific events in detail. They may recognize their previous parents, children, brothers and sisters and specific places from their previous life.

"You see, David, nothing is definite in life. For every rule there are exceptions," smiled the angel when he saw me thinking, quite frustratedly, why I don't remember my own past life events.

"Now, that the initial shock of life begins, let's move into the next stage.

"During the second stage of bonding, both the soul and the mini-souls of the cells have to adapt to each other quickly while the fetus has trillions of problems to solve. It isn't a simple nor an easy task to perform. The human soul, by now, has to take over, coordinating the rapid reproduction of new cells, promoting the fast growth and, at the same time, solve the many arising issues in the process of the bonding. Even if the development of the fetus seems only as a genetic technical process which is done automatically like a machine with the brain coordinating its growth, this is but part of the truth. Don't forget we are dealing with trillions of living creatures. The cells have their own needs, requirements, demands, refusals, maladaptation, genetic mistakes and many other issues that aren't solved by the genetic code or the brain's functions. There is some intelligence, indeed a very high intelligence, to create such an enormous complex as the body of an animal or that of a human being. Furthermore, the soul has to overcome his own adaptation shock, get acquainted and respond to the various needs and demands from trillions of mini-souls, and then establish quickly a permanent energy link between himself and the many souls of the nerve cells in the entire body. And if that isn't enough, the new soul has to establish a positive relationship with the mother's soul. Usually the mother's soul is very helpful and responsive to the needs of the new soul, but sometimes the reincarnating soul has to fight with the mother's soul, to awaken her to take care of herself in order to create better conditions and improve the fetus's growth. It is a frustrating situation for the fetus's soul to learn that he is being ignored, that there are some things which he just cannot change in the mother's physical and/or mental conditions.

"This stage starts almost immediately after the soul enters

the new fetus body, but in some maladjusted souls, this stage might begin up to two weeks from the time of entering into the body."

"What happens if the souls of the body cells don't like the kind of soul that enters them?" I asked the angel.

"If, for any reason, an adaptation between the new soul and the fetus cells' souls does not occur, then there is no future life for that mass of cells. The cells' souls cannot replace the big reincarnated soul. This actually means the death of that fetus in the womb. Therefore, it isn't a light decision to rebel against a new soul. Instinctively, the mini-souls of the body know that very clearly. It is a life and death decision to accept the new authority as best and as completely as they can. Being living entities, the cells can decide rapidly on many issues that will affect the life of that fetus for good. The soul needs this support. If there is no support, the soul has no control. This actually means a very defective new life form. In these cases, the soul usually leaves that body to die.

"Don't worry, David. It doesn't happen too often. In reality it is a rare incident, and although you should be aware of it, you wouldn't need to interact at this stage, because the souls go back almost instantly to the waiting area in the eteric level.

"In most cases, there is no problem and the second stage of bonding is smooth. Usually the mini-souls of the cells will welcome the new soul's authority, and they will comply with the requirements to establish a strong and healthy fetus to the best of their ability. It is actually a fight for life by the entire colony of cells and they are very aware of it.

"At this stage an intruder soul does not have room to be. The new soul, having already connections to the newly developed nerve cells has, by now, a good hold inside the fetus's body. This bond between the mini-souls of the nerve cells and the human's soul is getting stronger every day and continues the process throughout the entire body. The mother's soul still acts as a protector to the fetus's soul. She protects him against any intruder spirit who is less qualified for occupying the place of her baby's soul.

"Any intruder cannot be more qualified because it is not a question of a stronger spirit, but more of a matching between the soul and the body's mini-souls. Once there is an initial bond between a specific soul and a body, the big soul becomes part of that body, and from then on there is no way to replace him. If we disconnect a soul from his body, the body will die.

"We can conclude quite safely that inside the womb, there is no real danger to the fetus from any spirit possession. With time, the bonding is stronger, making it harder for any spirit to enter and possess that new body, even without the mother's soul's protection."

How did this bond between my body and my soul take place? What did it look like . . . ? I wondered.

The angel didn't wait long, he responded right away to my question.

"David, I'm glad that you follow. Let's answer your unspoken question right now.

"The soul who is manifested in the human body appears in his subatom 7 form, and, as you already know, this is composed of purer levels of subatoms down to subatom 1. The little souls of the body cells are in their subatom 7 form as well. They are also composed of subatoms down to subatom 1. The bond between the human soul and the fetus's cells' souls is first done in the astral level of the souls—the subatom 7 then it spread all the way down to subatom 1 level. But this is not all. The big soul also contains many pure living units connected to one another. And each of the little souls of the body's cells also is composed of pure living units which are connected to one another. Each living unit within the big soul sends a powerful supply of energy connection to a living unit in a cell. These connections are actually also the communication routes between the body and soul. How strong this connection is going to be— it depends on many factors. In general, the quality of bonding between the human soul and the entire fetus body will depend on two main factors: the quantity and the quality of the links between the human soul and the cells' souls.

"The human soul tries his best to attach himself to all of the living units of the fetus's cells through the cells of the nervous system.

"The quality of each connection can influence the quality of the whole bonding of body and soul. But, practically, not all connections are a 100 percent perfect for one of the many reasons of maladaptation between the human soul and that of the specific cells' souls.

"Sometimes a bad or a weak energy connection leaves room for errors. This may manifest as physical or mental disorders in the future of that individual. Of course, for the observer on the physical level, these diseases are going to look like the normal, familiar problems which a human being may suffer on Earth—a routine disease, usually as one of the degenerative diseases or a common mental disorder. Moreover, incomplete bonding between the human soul and the human body are among the chief reasons for another spirit to possess the body.

"Now that you know the basics of how the bonding is made, let's start with stage three of this process.

"This stage begins in a very dramatic way with the child's birth. The fetus is getting out of the protected environment of the womb. Whether the birth is natural or facilitated in a hospital—it is immaterial. Once the new baby is out, the baby's soul has another duty which is to facilitate the adaptation of the newborn baby to the new environment. It is a very demanding job. The new baby has to continue to grow at an enormous rate, learn new skills, communicate with new figures in his life and build his new defense mechanisms. These defense mechanisms include the physical one—which is the immune system for protecting his body—and the emotional one to be able to stand all the frustrations he will feel while encountering his new surroundings. At the same time, he also builds another defense mechanism—one that is against the many possible astral world's intruders, the opportunistic spirits who may wish to possess a body.

"This stage, which starts at birth, continues until about six to eight months after birth. It is the 'get acquainted' period. The soul learns the new environment from the baby point of view. He learns to recognize his own limitations and to establish further communication with his own body and brain.

"In this period, it is very rare that the newborn body will encounter an opportunistic soul. The reason is simple. At this stage, although without the umbrella of the mother's soul protection, the soul of the newborn baby is actively involved in the reinforcement of his communication with the entire colony of cells in his body. The soul who is properly reincarnated is clearly bonded, by now, to the cells' souls with clear, well-established links. This makes it hard for a possessing soul to enter. Without a proper bonding to the cells, a possessing soul has no place to hold, therefore, has no power to resist even the smallest attempt to be thrown out. By being thrown out, he also loses some of his already depleted soul energy. This ensures that if, and when, he reincarnates, that soul will have a much less fortunate life cycle. The majority of the souls within the astral level know intuitively that it is a risky business for them to attempt to enter a newborn baby. Therefore, usually, no attempt occurs at this stage.

"On the other hand, there is a very slim possibility that another, much bigger, nonhuman spirit will attempt to possess a newborn baby. That might happen when the reincarnated soul was dealing with very negative issues against humanity in his previous reincarnation, and therefore establishes bad links with its own body cells.

"If this occurs, a well-trained person, having the support of the guardian angels has to help. One day you will be able to help people with that type of spirit possession, David. It isn't dangerous in any way, and not at all scary. It is a very simple procedure. You will perform those activities with ease, whether the intruder souls are the souls of other humans who refused to reincarnate, or the spirits of other entities trying to experience the physical life, or acting as part of the Old Spirits interaction with the physical matter."

I was quiet. It scared me. It sounded like a serious matter although the angel presented it as a simple task to do and said that I would be able to perform it with the help from the Divine Forces. No, it sounds too crazy for me . . . I'm just a teenager in a marine school . . .

"Don't worry David," the angel reacted to my thought and smiled at me. Soon I felt the radiation of a loving energy that filled me with warmth and a secure sensation as if I were covered from within and throughout my soul body. I calmed down. Yes, I needed just that . . . He really feels for me . . . knows everything about me . . .

"David, now that you feel better, let's continue with the next stages of the soul bonding process.

"The fourth stage of this process starts from the age of six months after birth until the age of about ten to thirteen years. The soul in this stage is still in a very intensive adaptation process. The sexual changes in the adolescent boys and girls will be the end of this stage. By then, the soul has established more links of communication and protection between the many cells' souls and the human soul. The cells' souls are invoked to search for meaning in life. They are curious. After the initial shock of intense formation from a few cells into a complex structure, the little souls are starting to look for a meaning, a purpose in life, and they actually demand to be informed, loved and cared for by the bigger soul who entered as their big authority. Well, in reality, it is the part of the big soul to address and inform in a loving, protective way those little souls of the body's cells who, actually, invited him to enter and be part of them.

"As I told you, David, it might seem, initially, that the whole process of integration between the body cells and the soul of a person is done in an automatic mode, without much thinking or feeling involved. In reality, the genetic code for the growth of that human is a general framework, but without the proper communication and interaction between the human soul and the trillions of mini-souls of the cells, such a complex interaction would never be possible. The brain, theoretically, may be the answer to normal functions of the body, but not to the fulfillment of emotions of the body cells. They need someone who will be in a higher position to address their various needs, including their spiritual needs.

"This period is crucial to the wellness of the entire body and, eventually, the real basis of growth into adulthood. In this period of time, possession of the body might occur. It is still a rare occurrence at the beginning of this stage, but becomes more frequent when the person grows into sexual adulthood. It has nothing to do with sexuality. Nevertheless, when the body is reaching its maturity and then the body becomes more stabilized, the human soul invests less energy in the normal process of the daily life; instead, he tunes himself gradually to other activities mainly at the astral level of existence. Therefore, the frequency of bad connections of the soul with new growing cells is getting higher. This enables some possessing souls to enter into the young, but less attended physical body.

"In reality, about less than one percent of the entire possessed population are possessed during this stage. Out of those who are possessed during this stage, about 97 percent are in the ages of ten years or older. You can see for yourself that the young years of life are quite protected from possessive spirits.

"Now we come to the fifth stage. It is during this stage that most of the humans who have been possessed experience it.

"The fifth stage is actually the longest in the life of a person. It starts at the age of sexual maturity and ends when that person passes away into their reincarnation cycle, or as you simply call it, when that person dies. By now, the soul's attention is partially focused on the routine aspects of life, and mainly on his own interests. Many times this interest has nothing to do with the physical body.

"Remember, David, in order to stay balanced and healthy you must, as a soul, be focused as much as you practically can, on the wellness of your own body. In reality, it becomes quite boring for the soul to deal with the many trillions of cells and their enormous demands. Most of the souls of humanity on Earth tend to partially ignore those demands. In some other cases, a soul can become so detached from the body that he may forget to continue to occupy the entire body, its cells' population and its inner space. In such a case—which almost the entire of humanity can be categorized under—the door for spirits' possessions is open.

"As strange as it may seem to you initially, most humans have, at one time or another, possessing spirits in them; very much so as we can claim that all humans, at one time or another, are 'possessed' by some viruses or microbes. Whether the possession by these viruses or microbes happens for a short or longer period of time—that will depend on the immune system of that person which, in turn, depends on other conditions as well.

"Similarly it is with the possessive spirits. The better relationship the human soul has with his own cells' mini-souls, the faster that soul becomes aware of the possession and throws that spirit away within a very short time; but the worse the connection that the human soul has with his own cells' souls, the harder for that soul to take over his own body again. In this case, it is also less likely that the human soul will know how to react to the intruder. Furthermore, sometimes, due to poor communication between the body cells and the human soul, the human soul simply doesn't care about the possessing spirit who tries to hide the best he can in that body so that he wouldn't be thrown away. In most cases, the hiding 'guest' has, in reality, very little influence on the life of the `host'! In a small portion of the cases, the influence might be stronger. The possessed person may adapt to the negative emotional state of the `guest spirit'. In some cases this can lead to the development of mental disorders. Being depleted from body energy and vitality by a 'guest spirit' may lead also to some physical disorders. These happen due to the frustration of the body cells and the gradual energy intensification of the possessing spirit.

"In some rare conditions, another soul can replace the first one. Again, it does not happen very often, but, if for example, the body's soul stays too long in the astral level, then either the physical body dies or it creates an opening for another human soul to enter. In this case, that soul will not be a reincarnated one, but an intruder who was at the astral level. The intruder's soul, then, will bond with the cells of the few remaining open nerve cells and some muscle cells. This kind of bonding is much weaker than the natural bond which involved most of the neurons of the fetus. This phenomenon can occur for other reasons as well, usually due to problems within the cells's souls and the human reincarnating soul.

"Although the manifestations might seem to you, right now, as very serious, in most cases the possessing spirits are very easy to send away, especially after you will learn the simple, but effective, methods of depossession. Best is to instruct the possessing spirits to complete their reincarnation cycle. In such a case, you help two human souls at the same time. If you cannot help that possessing spirit for whatever reason, ask for help from the guardian angels. They will be happy to help. But it is very unlikely for you to have difficulties in the act of depossession.

"The possession of a human body by a guest spirit is a natural phenomenon which usually occurs for a limited, short period of time. Almost every human being has experienced one or more of these spirit possessions, without any damage or even being aware of it at all.

"Now let's look at the spirit possession from another aspect. It has nothing to do with rituals, spirit communications through the seance board, or any of the many tales you might hear from time to time. It has to do with daily negligence of the body by its big soul. If the basic communication between the soul and the body cells is generally positive, then there is no problem at all. Otherwise, if there is poor communication between the soul and his body, it is an issue which will require the assistance of someone who knows how to depossess a spirit from a body, and who can redirect the person's soul to communicate better with his own body cells.

"After the fifth stage the process reaches its end. Stage six is the shortest stage of all. It is the separation of the soul from the body. As you know, David, this might happen at any age, under any circumstance. To some, this stage might be very sad and traumatic; to others, it can be a happy relief from some hardship. As you experienced with Sarah's case, you will encounter a wide variety of emotions at this stage, mainly due to the connections of the soul's emotions with the people they leave behind. Some may feel that there is unfinished business to complete; yet, others may wish to take revenge on persons who were unfair or evil to them. . .

"There are very few human souls who acknowledge the suffering of their own cells' mini-souls. They may participate in the terrible pain and fear of the souls they are leaving behind—the profound desperation of those trillions of mini-souls of the human body cells. Once the soul leaves, the links are broken for good between them and their own master soul. They know very well that this is their end as well. It is the death of trillions of faithful, obedient cells and the departure of those tiny souls who are going to continue their cycle of reincarnation as well at some other time, but the fear of the unknown is there. If the soul of the departed person would only acknowledge their loyal service, their complete selfless life for the service of their master—the bigger soul of the human being, who takes things so much for granted—all will feel better.

There is a reason for this detached approach of the human soul to his body. It is rooted in the history of the human race's evolution on Earth." I became curious now.

"David, in one of our next meetings here, I will tell you more about it," the angel promised and then continued. "As a future helper you will need to approach those whom you are going to help as part of the big cycle of life. It is a simple, normal and natural event in the life cycle. Separations are sad moments, but this is not the end. It is part of a long evolutionary process of the human race in particular and the whole Universe in general. This is important for you to remember, so that you can help those who pass away to continue their reincarnation cycle. For you it is going to be a natural fact of life, while for most of those whom you will help it is a complete mystery. They will need your support and the knowledge that you are getting now.

"David, you have learned about one aspect of the life cycles in terms of the soul's bonding to the body. There is much more to learn about life, about the evolution and the destiny of humanity. But for now just remember that to participate in the life cycle, the soul, or any other living units or life form in the Universe, has to agree to play the game of life. There is a free will, but sometimes this free will is so deeply implanted inside of the living units of the soul that, for the conscious mind, it might be nonexistent or forgotten.

"All of these life forms, such as human beings, once forgetting their own choice to participate in the life cycle activities may think, when the times become tough, or when they suffer to some degree: 'I didn't ask to be born . . . I'd rather die . . . who needs this cruel life' and so forth.

"The reality is stronger than any claim or protest. As a fact, no one really has to live in the physical form, but, the other options are much worse than the life decision in spite of any suffering.

"If any soul would truly refuse to reincarnate, he would

simply discontinue his cycles of evolution. No one is going to force him but himself.

"Every participant in the cycle of physical life knows very well that there is a great investment to make in order to participate in the present cycle of physical life activities. Yet they choose it, no matter what. It is a desperate decision sometimes, but a very strong one. You will detect this commitment for life even in those who commit suicide. Some of them cognitively think that by this they will cease to exist. In reality, deep inside, they know that there is after life existence and they wrongfully believe that by changing their circumstances, they are going to face a better life in the next cycle. Unfortunately for them, as you are going to find, there is no solution in the suicide action. These poor souls lose life energy, life forces, which causes some living units to leave them. Therefore, these specific souls are going to match a less fortunate fetus body and life cycle in the future; thus, worsening their conditions in their next reincarnation.

"Most life forms in the Universe, including the human souls, choose consciously to live and participate in the evolutionary cycle of the Universe—partly because the alternatives aren't better. There is no escape in the cosmic reality, no other valid options to take, in spite of the free will of each living unit in the soul.

"There are already enormous quantities of living units in the empty space that, for some reasons, have never entered into the cycle of a conscious life form. They are waiting in a semi-sleep state for eternity—waiting with no real manifestation of life, with no meaning, no desire, no happiness nor sadness, but a plain, emotionless waiting stage. Would you or any one of the life forms, human or others, agree to this endless meaningless life? The answer, David, is simply NO. Once the living units at any level of existence become aware of the full conscious life, there is no turning back. They will prefer, thousands of times, a life with suffering, pain and frustration—but with some hope—to the endless, emotionless life in space for eternity, until the complete unification of the entire life in the Universe with the Creator."

"When is this unification going to happen? And how—"

"We shall talk about the Universe destiny much more deeply in the coming lectures, David. You can go back into your body now, but first go for a little tour in the astral world. I will see you here tomorrow at the same time."

Before I could complete my question, the angel disappeared.

Looking down at the blue sea, I decided to explore the Mediterranean, so I glided for a while. Soon I witnessed the enormous astral life again. Many spirits were gliding just like me. Some others were floating motionlessly in the air. Part of these spirits seemed to be of humans, others of animals, and yet others appeared like strange creatures. Observing the water, I realized that some spirits are there, among the fish and the enormous life of the sea. Gliding fast right above the sea felt fascinating. Soon I noticed my cord—the cord that was connecting my soul to my body. I didn't ask the angel about that . . . Is it connected to the living units in my nerves' cells?

I suddenly missed all the little cells' souls that I had left in my body. Are they . . . afraid every time I leave the body? Can some other spirit, an intruder, enter my body while I'm out? I must ask the angel these questions . . .

In a flash, I found myself back in my body fully awake, thinking about Lamdiel's lecture. I couldn't close my eyes for a while but, when I did, I kept thinking about my cells. Each one feels like a separate entity with its emotions and wishes . . . living in a big world . . . in me . . . They really depend on me . . . on the connection they made with my soul . . . We are united until the end of my life cycle . . . Is this why the angel Upiel asked me to always send love to my body, and promise to the body cells that I would come back after my out-of-body activities . . . ?

A special sensation suddenly filled my whole being. It was a radiation from within myself . . . feelings of love . . . not only from my heart but from everywhere in my body. Do the little souls thank me for caring about them more in depth now . . . ?

The next day, I woke up feeling extremely refreshed and happy. Looking down at my body, I felt lots of warmth and excitement. I couldn't wait to be there again, above the Mediterranean with Lamdiel. He really opened a new awareness in me. I had been changing from day to day—growing stronger from within.

Night time arrived, and the usual command "Its lights-off time" was heard. Everyone went to sleep. It was quiet. I took a few deep breaths. Soon I was gliding above the sea again ready for my next lesson with Lamdiel.

* * *

It is the irony of life on your planet that
many who fight another ethnic group,
religion, or any other group of people today,
don't know that they, themselves, were actually
an active part of that very same group; they
don't know that they actually are fighting now
against values that were sacred to them, and
against people they loved from their previous
lives—whether their own children, grandchildren
and, sometimes, a spouse or a dear friend who
may still live among that group of people.
Yes, you humans are all the same—one big family.
There is no place for hate towards each other.

* * *

12
Lives Inside Lives

"**D**avid," Lamdiel greeted me with a radiant smile, "don't worry. It is safe for you to continue and to leave your body. When you leave your body the way you were taught, you are still connected to your whole body. No intruders' souls can really enter into your body because, when you are out of your body during your life on the physical level, you are still well-connected to the little souls of your physical body cells. You were right. The energy cord that is attached to you and your physical body is actually the extension of trillions of energy bonds between your soul and the little cells' souls. These connections keep your body alive. These bonds are broken naturally at the end of the life cycle when the soul departs from the body in order to start a new life cycle."

"Thank you, I really worried about it. But what about the little souls of the cells?"

"They also go through the same process. Each of the little souls departs from its cell and gets ready for its next life cycle, into a newly forming cell. They have their own guardian angels and spiritual helpers, and once these cells' souls complete their life cycle—which is very much shorter than yours—they get assistance with their reincarnation process, similar to the one of humans.

"Now, David, let's start with the lesson. There is a lot for you to learn about life. Just be open in your study. Soon you will be able to easily visualize everything I'm telling you, as if you see with your own eyes."

"Life in any form is a compound of smaller lives which are

composed of much smaller lives, and so on. Life instincts are basically the same for all life forms in the Universe, although their manifestations may be different on each of the ten levels of existence or even among the life forms of the same level. For example, you the humans, animals and plants live within the same level of existence—within the physical level—but there are many differences between the lives of humans, animals, plants or viruses, for example. Nevertheless, there are many similarities as well. These apply to all of the life forms anywhere in the Universe.

"A simple life form, as a general rule, feels the urge to grow and evolve into the maximum potential that can be achieved in its life cycle. It is an inner wish of each and every life form, not only a genetic command. This urge creates new lives by a process of unification and formation. The evolution of simple life forms is done by uniting themselves, in a specific way, to each other and then attracting a much more highly developed spirit in order to evolve. Each of the smaller life forms that exists in a larger life complex has the same instincts of life as the larger life form it lives in. Let's take for example a life form that you are already familiar with—the human being.

"You already have learned about the living cells in your body. In reality, other microorganisms live in the human body as well. At school you were taught about the many microorganisms which are living in the human colon. The human body needs them as much as they need the human body. Some other microorganisms which live inside the body aren't so friendly to their big host. Regardless of their role in the human body, microorganisms which live inside it have no recognition of the intelligence and feelings of the bigger life form that hosts them. These microorganisms—which are actually types of cells who live in the human body as if it were their entire world—do have their life structures, some conscious level, feelings and communication between each other, as all life forms in the Universe have. They live, multiply, and then die to continue their evolutionary cycle. Observing them carefully, we realize that inside of the microorganisms exist other types of smaller lives. Science is aware of the negative and destructive smaller life forms which penetrate these microorganisms. They were named viruses. In reality, there are also some viruses that live in cooperation with the microbes and other types of living cells. Some of the viruses are essential to the life of their hosts which are single cell units or the microbes of various types.

"Those simpler life forms, the viruses, which are living a major part of their life inside the cells of their hosts, also have emotions, feelings and simple communication skills with each other. But, they totally ignore the lives of their hosts as valid life forms. For each one of them, it is just Nature . . . a place where they have to learn how to adjust by means of adaptation and fast mutation. All of this is through a short period of life cycles which, in turn, create many cycles of genetic mutations in accordance with the universal evolutionary laws.

"This simple life form isn't the end of the story. Much smaller life forms are actually finding their place in the viruses' bodies as well. These small and simple entities are known to science as simple groups of amino acids, which create simple groups of proteins. Science does not consider them as being alive . . . Well, even if science denies their living state, the facts do not change—these simpler life forms are very much alive. They do reproduce themselves, do have life instincts and do support or destroy the viruses. Like humans, they have the wish to live and expand.

"The reality of life goes well beyond this point. Proteins are actually composed of many little molecules which are very much alive and live in a very well defined way and structure, but some of these molecules, believe it or not, have their own agenda about life. They choose to participate in the proteins as an important contribution to their lives; others choose to ignore their host, and become unwelcome guests, actually destroying those proteins. This is very much like some microbes become harmful to humans; some viruses, to the cells; and some proteins, to the viruses.

"The next group is even harder to accept as alive due to the wrong belief that conscious awareness belongs only to the higher living complexes. This is a very wrong concept. In reality, atoms which compose the molecules are alive, have their own emotions and life instincts. Some of them are beneficial to the molecule that is part of the protein, that is part of the virus, that is part of the cells that are part of a larger life form like the human body. Each one of them has its own spirit bonded to each particle, and together they create the foundation for a higher life form with a much bigger spirit.

"Life is much more than what can be seen with or without the tools your scientists have developed. Life has many faces, many levels, forms and sizes.

"David, all of these compounded life manifestations on your physical level are real, the same as you feel yourself as real and alive. They are living in a complex of compounded lives inside other lives. One day you will be able to see and communicate with the spirits of cells, microbes, viruses, proteins and others."

It amused me, but I continued to listen carefully.

"Yes, David, conceiving the wider scope of life, you will realize that life is a unique force in the Universe. It is very much like other forces that are already known to your scientists today—the electromagnetic force, gravity and the weak and strong forces of the atom. Your planet's present scientific point of view can be considered only as a partial understanding of reality, especially because of its own limitations and opposition to anything which has to do with life energy as a unique force in the Universe. Medicine of the future will have to address the many forces of life for what they call a genetic cure of many diseases. This process will be done very much like that of the extraterrestrials who artificially promoted the acceleration of Earth humans' cognitive minds, while addressing the many differences at the atom level. It was a must for them in order to be able to overcome the changes in the genetic code of the apes in such a way that would match the genetic differences of a more advanced brain of humans."

At that moment I began to think about it. What was really done to our ancestors . . . ? What is the life like on other planets where those extraterrestrials live . . . ? Do they watch us from there . . . ? Do they care . . . ? And if so, then why? . . .

"David," the angel answered my thoughts, "in due time you will meet entities and humanoids from other planets who are much more advanced than the humans on your planet. Then you will be taught some of their technology and steps of evolution. But be patient. What you learn now will prepare you for your future study. It's OK. You are allowed to think whatever you wish, David, but keep listening as well and continue to visualize everything I say.

"Now that you have learned about the concept of lives inside lives inside life . . . you may feel like a walking world." The angel smiled. "But what about yourself, David? Are you a part of a bigger life form?"

I became alarmed. I grasped what he was going to tell me. But it was hard for me to accept it.

"The answer is YES. You are right, David. You humans are part of planet Earth's life. Your planet is made out of atoms. Each one of them contains living units or little spirits. The whole planet, including its atmosphere, water, plants, animals and all the living species on it, including humans, are attached by their spirits to the spirit of the planet Earth. This is a giant spirit which has a simple structure at the present. The living species on Earth represent the living evolution of the planet. And the human beings represent the most advanced function of the planet. If it is hard for you to perceive this idea, think about the little microorganisms inside your body. They conceive life around them similarly to the way you human beings conceive your lives on planet Earth, without being aware at all that your planet has its own conscious life, and that all life forms on the planet are the manifestation of its life."

"Wow!" I became very excited.

"Yes, David, but this is not the end. Your planet is part of a much bigger life form—the Solar System, which is part of a galaxy, which is part of a cluster of galaxies. There are many clusters in the Universe. In the cluster to which your planet belongs, the Solar System is considered an atom. Millions of star systems like your Solar System create the galaxy to which you belong. Humans on your planet call it the Milky Way because of the way it looks from Earth. The Milky Way is like a molecule in the cluster level. Many thousands of galaxies are actually grouped together into what you call a cluster. Can you imagine this size?"

I kept visualizing everything as if I were watching a movie about giants.

The angel smiled. "Many clusters build a supercluster which is equivalent to matter in your level. There are many superclusters made out of clusters. Each can be attached to an enormous matching spirit from the divine level, the 2nd level. Not all of them are yet connected to their matching spirits. It is an evolutionary process. Those superclusters may not look to you as living creatures; nevertheless, they are. Of course they are totally different from what you perceive as life, but if you can understand the life of your planet Earth, you will be able to grasp their lives as well."

The angel paused for a moment and then continued. "If this seems so huge to you, can you imagine the size of the Creator?

"All of the life forms in the cluster level, including the cluster that you belong to, are actually part of the largest level—the finite, the 10th level of the Universe. The 10th level and the infinite level, the 1st level, which is composed out of pure living units, subatoms 1 and energy, form together the entire

Universe which is also our Creator.

"Wow! He is really big. It's hard to conceive His size."

"Yes, David, for now it is more than your ability to imagine. We are all manifestations of His life. He is everything in the Universe, including the superclusters of galaxies, all the matter, the space, the living units and all of the life forms."

I was quiet. My awareness widened altogether. I had changed that night. Suddenly I felt strange. I am part of a huge living thing . . . How do I look inside that Creator? . . . Not even like a small atom . . . What is a human being compared to all the giant life forms ? . . . We are really nothing . . . Now I'm being taught how to be a helper to the human race, so I will be able to help in the evolutionary process . . . but being so small, are we considered by this giant Creator at all . . . ?

"Yes, David," the angel reacted to my thoughts. "Each one of us, every little life form, is part of the Creator. Therefore, each and every one of us does count. The Creator has His own code of living. You may call it the laws of Nature, or the laws of the Creator, as you wish. They are all part of the regulatory system of the Universe—of the Creator. The Creator's laws keep everything in balance. This eventually influences each one of us in the Universe including me, you and all of the other life forms. Even if it cannot be imagined as such, the whole Universe is in perfect equilibrium. You, for example, don't normally zoom in occasionally to check every tiny cell or atom in your body. When you feel pain you become aware through your nervous system of an existing problem but, even then, you don't really check each and every cell in the painful area. Nevertheless, you do care. It's part of your whole body. The Creator doesn't feel pain, but He is constantly being informed through the galaxy energy and the clusters—of which your planet is a part—about existing problems. These issues are taken care of indirectly through His regulatory system.

"As for us, we know, that the Creator lives forever, but all the living forms inside of Him do have cycles of life and death except for the 1st and 10th levels. This is how the Creator re-news Himself and how He improves Himself through a constant evolutionary process that we all are a part of. Yes, David, we all contribute to it, but we all absolutely benefit from it as well.

13
Laws of Nature—The Factors
That Regulate Life

"The Creator's codes of living, the laws of Nature, as I told you are affecting everyone's destiny in the Universe. These laws, or codes of Nature, are dynamic and constantly interacting with each other."

I became curious. "What are they? . . . how can they affect me . . . or anyone else?"

The angel smiled. "Let's start with some of the forces that affect everything in the Universe. Some of these are already familiar to your scientists.

"All living and nonliving matter in our Universe obey the following major forces which apply separately to every level of existence. In short, they are the electromagnetic force, the gravity force, and the two forces of the atom which are the weak and strong forces of the atom. Similar forces apply to each subatom from 1 to 7. On each level, these four forces have proportional intensity and do not affect other levels nor are they influenced by other levels.

"Life is another force in the Universe. Life Force or, in short, LF is the main energy that is found in every living unit. It describes the intensity, the inner strength of any life form, or spirit in the Universe. In order to make it simple to understand, you don't need the exact measurements of the Life Force, but only to remember that the total energy needed to keep one living unit alive is called one Life Force (1LF). This energy is impossible to see or to be evaluated on your level. However, there is an indirect way to sense—not to calculate—the intensity energy of any life form. You do it indirectly through sensing one of the other factors which are found inside the living units.

"For you humans, it is important to know that during your life on the physical level you can gain more Life Force or energy when you follow the universal codes which are a part of you. In short, live with love and harmony with yourself and others. The main gain or loss of energy— Life Force—will cause living units to join or to leave the soul. This is usually carried on when you reincarnate into your matching next life; thus influencing the quality of your next life cycle as well. This process applies to every life form in the Universe. It is part of destiny.

"Each living unit in the Universe contains, besides Life Force, a few other factors that constantly influence each life form. One of them is called the Creator Factor or CF. The Creator Factor is the Creator's code of ethics, fairness, justness, and the cosmic moral values within every single living unit. The Creator Factor is a mental code made of energy with no physical manifestations or descriptions. It has a constant force that cannot be regulated within the living unit itself. Only the unlimited powers of the Creator can regulate its activity which has not been changed, as far as I know, for many trillions of years.

"This factor is hard, or impossible, to evaluate in measured units of any kind. For simplicity, we assume that each living unit in the Universe contains one unit of Creator Factor, similar to Life Force. In short, we call it 1CF. The CF units match the quantity of living units within a specific spirit. It describes the total energy CF intensity in each life form in the Universe. The intensity of the Creator Factor, in contrast to the Life Force, can be sensed by many. Therefore, it is the real evaluation tool of the energy intensity of other life forms in the Universe. This is the energy you sense when you evaluate other spirits around you.

"The destiny of a person or any life form is backed up by

the Creator Factor within each soul. Life forms cannot run away from themselves, from the code of fairness, justness, and the cosmic moral in their own spirits. Those who behave in a way contrary to the Universe's code of ethics, do punish themselves. The Creator Factor units within the living units are actually in charge of this effect. Humans sometimes call it the superconscious within themselves. They feel it deep inside, for example, when they hurt another human or a life form for other than survival purposes. This is true for the other levels of existence as well, David. It is one of the factors that affects life and destiny in the Universe. In reality, it is a clear demonstration for the existence of the Creator within every living thing. It is one of the inner regulatory tools of life. Nevertheless, not all humans or life forms in the Universe follow their own inner consciousness—the CFs in their spirits—but no one can escape for long from the effects of the CFs on their destiny.

"The Creator Factor is not of much use for the way your science perceives life now. Science cannot experiment with the Creator Factor as you would experiment, for example, with the electromagnetic force. Nevertheless, it is an intense and clear force within all life in the Universe.

"We can also describe the Creator Factor as part of the life code within the life forms on all levels of existence. Partly, you may view it as one of the primary forces that affects the destiny of the entire Universe through its living units. The Creator Factor within the living units is an important part of the Destiny laws which are an essential part of the laws of Nature. Destiny is actually the total of all the powers in the Universe that lead a person, or any other life form, to act or become what he is. But for now, David, we do not need to enter into the CFs more deeply than that. It is enough that you understand the concept.

"Another important aspect that influences each one of us is the I Factor, or IF. This factor is an energy that the Creator implanted in each and every living unit at the infinite level.

This factor influences each and every one of the other dimensions in the Universe. This factor was imprinted in such a way that it became the motivation factor for life at any given time, in any life form. Yes, David, this factor is the root of all our needs and wishes. This factor is the source for happiness, joy, and fulfillment in each and every living unit and every life form in the Universe. It is the source for the need to love and be loved, to be devoted and to be accepted by others. It is the reason for seeking fulfillment, success and recognition. For you humans and all other life forms, it is also the source for addictions and obsessions on each level of the human's activity, whether emotional addiction, physical or chemical addiction, and behavior or intellectual addictions, including all types of obsessive behavior that are related to seeking pleasure and comfort.

"In contrast to the Creator Factor which is also located in each living unit, the I Factor is changeable in intensity. It varies from zero to one hundred percent of influence in each living unit. Some stimulations do activate its core function, and at that time any human, or any life form, feels at the top of his happiness and satisfaction. When this factor is inactive, a human or any life form feels depressed and as if separated from life. As strange as it might seem, we, all the life forms in the Universe, don't really have much control over this factor. It works completely independently from our wishes because it is imprinted in the core of each spirit at the infinite level of every living unit. It is also regulated by the Creator Factor, the CF, and other laws of destiny."

"But you said that there are some stimulations which activate this factor so one can feel good."

"Yes, David, in a way the I Factor can be activated. When it happens, it improves one's feelings. This applies to the whole human race and other lives as well. There are quite a few things that can stimulate this I Factor. One of them is the gaining of the basics of anything we think about or need in the level we are at, such as the basic needs for survival, love, affection, being loved and accepted and appreciated by others of the same species.

"Fulfillment of the reproduction requirements according to the specific need of one's race, and securing the future of that race through the evolutionary process is another aspect that stimulates the I Factor.

"The I Factor is the source of love. A big part of life is devoted to keeping the I Factor at its maximum activity.

"Did you ever wonder what happens when you are happy? The energy of the IF in each of the living units in your soul is being activated and then radiates to the Life Force—which is also the awareness of the I—that you are happy. The wish to stay emotionally bonded with others of your type, to grow and evolve, and to correct bonds between living units of your body and soul, is also within this factor. David, love is one of the main tools for feeling this IF in action. That's why love is so important for everyone's health all over the Universe.

"Fulfilling, reaching our goals at any level we are at, can stimulate the IF as well. This includes building or developing something, reaching some desired places or activities, or getting the information we seek. Yes, David, these are other aspects which stimulate the I Factor in us.

"Relaxation, as one of the main ways for satisfaction, is also another way to trigger the I Factor. Therefore one feels good while meditating. Many life forms can stay in semi-sleep state for many millions of years. The problem with this state is that it does not promote the acceleration of the evolutionary process. Therefore, in a way, it reduces the effect of the other aspects which are promoted by this factor.

"The I Factor balances the effect of the Creator Factor. It is being stimulated by doing good and helping others, sacrificing for others, as well as by working and doing things that are considered as a push ahead to the evolutionary process.

"As you can see from this partial list, the activity of the I

Factor is enormous in one's life. There is much more to know about the effects which are originated by this factor on the mental and physical health of humans. Without proper stimulation, the IF reduces its intensity, so the ability to feel happy or good is reduced as well. Therefore, any living form will do its best to continue to stimulate this factor.

"This IF is basically a positive stimulation which leads to a well-defined social formation. The I Factor enables all species, including humanity, to evolve into higher levels of life, supporting each other as a united species with love and devotion.

"The I Factor is, in reality, influenced by many primary and secondary factors. Therefore, it is easy for a life form to avoid or not to feel the entire happiness that it wants to have in life. At times, the need for stimulating the I Factor is so strong that in order to fulfill this factor, a human, or any other life form, may commit crimes against his own race.

"The reason that people on Earth are vulnerable in fulfilling this factor at the expense of their own destiny is an issue that we will discuss later.

"In short, David, the IF is one of the most important factors affecting the life quality of all the life forms. It is the main factor that all other factors have to work hard at in order to balance its demand for fulfillment.

"In a way, you can look at the I Factor and the Creator Factor which influence, or are parts of, each one's destiny as similar to the many social laws or codes you have in various places on Earth, the ones which help or force each individual or group to behave and act according to the social code of that place.

"The difference between your social laws and those of the CF and the I Factor is that these two are the inner regulators of life behavior. They were designed to enforce the Creator's laws from within each living unit. They are an integral part of the soul which affects everyone, either in the present life cycle or the next ones."

"Now, David, I hear you asking, and rightly so, why then is there so much crime, cruelty and unjustness within humanity? Isn't it a sign which contradicts these two factors inside our living units?"

I was again surprised. It seems that I had not gotten used to the ability of the angel to hear me thinking. He knows my deepest doubts and thoughts . . . I wonder if I will be able to do just that in the future . . .

"David," he looked at me with a smile, acknowledging my feelings, "let's continue and you will understand why there is so much unjustness and cruelty in life in spite of the superconscious justness which is part of the Creator Factor in every life form.

"Free Will—this is the real answer to your question about unjustness within humanity and other life forms on Earth and everywhere in the Universe. It is another fundamental aspect of life. The freedom of choice is the only way that any life form can exercise its independent existence. This is done by making one's own decisions and choices, or even one's own mistakes. This freedom isn't without a control, nor without a good reason. If you as a species want to grow faster in the evolutionary scale, you must do it in a certain way, using the trial and error process, while being open to the superconscious mind which acts as a regulator.

"The conscious Universe is created in a way which really allows for a maximum freedom of choice to all life forms, but within strict limitations. Part of it is the adjustment by the feelings and energies of justness in the CFs within the living units of these life forms. No force nor use of power can be effective in the long run on any life form, even if it may seem to be a situation that can be changed. Any actions and decisions that are made by free will during one's life affect one's destiny. In turn they affect the destiny of all humanity, since humanity has a collective life and influence in the evolutionary direction humanity goes according to the universal laws of Nature. In order to enrich yourself and your community, group, race or species, you must live a LOVING, DEVOTED and LOYAL LIFE to the entire society, after loving and being positive to yourself. Those who choose to act against themselves or others, ignoring the inner requirements of the CF about justness, will face the consequences of their own actions. Their destinies will be then encountered in a few ways during their lives in their physical level or after. Depending on the way they used their free will, they may face a retaliation from others, either on the personal level or through the justness system of that place, such as a family, a tribe or a court punishment system. If, for whatever reason, these individuals manage to escape from the punishment they justly deserve for their wrongdoings, then comes the more amazing thing in life—the universal justness of the Creator Factor which will force them to balance their lives by self-inflicted punishment which is actually a lesson that helps them to learn, so that they will continue to evolve. It happens so in each and every species all over the Universe in accordance with that species' unique evolutionary needs. The self-inflicted punishment is proportionate in severity for any wrongdoing. It is not always seen by others around as such. Nevertheless, it is a direct response for acting against Nature's requirements for fairness. This influences the evolutionary process in the Universe. Choosing to behave with love and fairness to oneself and others does count as well. It activates the I Factor within the spirit, bringing or triggering the inner joy and happiness. It also accelerates one's own well-being and evolutionary process within the limit of the collective destiny of the species and the specific group one belongs to. Yes, the results of the choices and actions taken with free will are carried after life as well. The next law of Nature may explain to you how.

"The destiny of any life form in the Universe is also influenced by the law of perfect cycles. All matter and life events, including the evolutionary process, are going into advanced cycles, similar to the course of a tire mounted on a car. The tire does create a perfect cycle but at the same time moves the car some distance ahead. In our case it is toward the unification of all matter and life in the Universe, closing the enormous cycle created by the Creator.

"This law is actually affecting the course of evolution in many ways. For now, we can consider it as the law for repetition of events in everything, including past, present and future life reincarnations. It is the tool that adjusts the life activity of any life form. The laws of Destiny, such as getting the rewards or lessons for any action, are interacting with the IF and the CF within each spirit, and are manifested in the perfect cycles.

"The law of perfect cycle leads to a build-up of talents. This assists in establishing a better life in one's next reincarnation. Each person does carry his achievements or lessons into the next life cycle. There are many areas in life to evolve in. Each person chooses the aspect of improvement that best suits his needs. These needs and talents are different from each other— not necessarily better or worse. Each contributes to the general evolutionary process of humanity on Earth.

"David, now listen to the following examples. They are all activated by the law of perfect cycle. People face it every day on your planet, but not all humanity is really aware of it.

"Those who have been dedicating their lives to acquiring more knowledge and wisdom will further develop their wisdom during their lives, and in the next lifetime they will be born with a better IQ and a better start in this aspect, providing they haven't used their knowledge against humanity and the life forms around them. Others, whose main activities are involved in developing their athletic skills will see the results in their present life cycle and will reincarnate into stronger bodies in their next life cycle, providing they haven't used their own strength against other humans during their present lives. People who make efforts to accumulate assets in their lives will be born into a wealthy life cycle similar to the one they left behind, but only if this accumulation of wealth was not achieved through the evilness of depriving other humans, or going against the laws of Nature. Others who mainly activate their emotions of dedication and love, or generously have been giving to others, will reach a higher ability of receiving and giving love. They will usually have the ability to help or heal others in their next life cycle.

"In short, David, each area in life has its satisfaction and reward. Some people make efforts in developing several specific areas of interest in their lives. Their achievements will be carried into their next reincarnation. Whatever field, or skill, is activated by a person during his life cycle—if done with love toward oneself and others, and with feeling of completion—it will help develop that person in this aspect/s during his present lifetime, and the main result will be seen in his next life cycle. One can reincarnate into a completely different, a much better life than the present one, according to what he has achieved by his present life cycle."

"Do people reincarnate into the same family, group or race they belonged to in their previous reincarnation?"

"Yes and no, David. It varies according to the destiny of that person, according to the rewards or the lessons one carries from his previous life cycle, and according to the general needs of the human evolution at that time. Many people do continue the reincarnation cycles in the same ethnic group to which they belonged in their previous lives. Other humans do reincarnate into other groups as well.

"One can be born on the north side of Earth and then, in the next reincarnation, the same soul can reincarnate into a family who lives in the south, east, or in the west part of the planet. One can be white in this lifetime and then be black, red or yellow in his next life cycle. One can reincarnate into a female body, although he was in a male body in his previous life, while another can reincarnate into a male body although that soul was in a female body in his previous life. One can belong to a certain religion in this lifetime, and then be born into a family who observes a different religion.

"It is the irony of life on your planet that many who fight another ethnic group, religion, or any other group of people today don't know that they, themselves, were actually an active part of that very same group; they don't know that they actually are fighting now against values that were sacred to them, and against people they loved from their previous lives—whether their own children, grandchildren and, sometimes, a spouse or a dear friend who may still live among that group of people. Yes, you humans are all the same—one big family. There is no place for hate towards each other. The more a person fights against a group or an idea, the more likely he will reincarnate into the very same group which he has fought against, and will face the hate and cruelty towards himself—as a victim—whether he reincarnates into the same group to which he belonged, or into the opposite group or religion. It is part of the lessons one goes through in order to be able to better evolve. The law of perfect cycle and the other laws of Nature are powerful. The rewards or lessons are always coming back, whether one is aware of these laws or not.

"On the soul level, during one's life, the wrongdoing person enters into a process of self-evaluation by the CF in his own living units. If the wrongdoings were significant, surpassing the balanced life of that person, then a conflict of view between the living units of the soul arises. This conflict between the basic core of the soul and the newly joined life force will eventually cause some of the living units within that soul to leave. That soul will lose living units. This loss can occur partially during one's life cycle, but the major loss is usually being carried into the next reincarnation.

"Practically, it means that in the next reincarnation, that soul will fit a less capable, and often less fortunate, living person, with very good chances of encountering similar events in his new reincarnation. But this time he may encounter that negative situation or event from the opposite side of a similar event. I will give you an example to make it clearer.

"Let's assume that a criminal, during the course of a crime activity, robbed an old lady. He managed to escape, in such a way without being caught, so that no one knows about his criminal activity. He apparently escaped from any punishment from the society or the law at that place.

"Now let's review what really is going to happen to that criminal: By not getting a response from society, he then has to activate the laws of Nature, responding to the Creator Factor—the justness within the self. In addition to the self-inflicted punishment that this person will bring to himself in the form of doing other criminal activity, this time subconsciously, that criminal will leave enough signs for him to be caught. He will also induce other self-inflicted punishment, such as entering into an accident, fighting or losing his own money, letting others steal from him, and so forth. Also, this criminal activity will cause his own body to rebel against his twisted mind; thus, bringing some physical ailment, such as cancer, arthritis, and any other systemic disease—a guarantee to make him suffer.

"It is very likely that in the next reincarnation that criminal will be born into a weaker body, will face more negative issues in his next life, and will encounter violent crimes performed against him.

"David, the laws of Nature do regulate everything in the Universe and were designed to ensure total equilibrium. As I told you, they do affect everyone's destiny. So even though we do have free will, and can choose to act or think the way we do, we still have to face the consequences of justness, as encoded in the Creator Factor in the living units of our spirits.

"Now, let's look at another example, but this time, of a person who is being cruel to his own family and his wife. He gets away with it during his present life. The next time he will reincarnate, the role will change. That person will reincarnate as a weak man who will very likely be abused by his father or other adult figures in his early life. The early abuse is a preparation for that person to acquire the 'right' victim's attitudes for him to choose the 'right' hateful spouse—a perfect cycle.

"We may look at these perfect cycles as punishments, but these are actually lessons which are designed to regulate life in the Universe. Don't take these examples in a wrong way, David. It does not mean that every person who is suffering on Earth today was necessarily an evil or cruel person in the previous reincarnation. This cause and effect law is responsible for about twenty percent of the suffering of life forms all over the Universe. Another reason for suffering is for the wrongs done earlier during one's life cycle. This accounts for about twenty percent of all suffering of life forms in the Universe. About another twenty percent of those who suffer are individuals or life forms who were good to themselves and others, and who really followed the inner laws of Nature. In their cases the suffering is an endurance tool to help them grow more into a higher, better life form. For example, a person had been devoted to his family, mainly living a simple life, being always positive with himself and others, having shown mainly love and devotion to his family, friends and country. As the result of an accident, he has many serious injuries which cause great pain before his death. We might now ask the question, if the laws which affect destiny are so balanced, how come this person had such a misfortune? In this case it might be that this person needed the suffering experience in order to evolve and grow into a better life form in the next reincarnation, either in the physical level or the purer ones."

"But how?" I just didn't understand that unfair point.

"The suffering makes one become more aware of the Creator Factor in his soul. This helps one to be even more considerate with others, and with the laws of Nature, and consequently to gain more energy into his soul.

"About another twenty percent pay the price of their family, tribe, country or the entire species' wrongdoing. That includes something which may not look like wrongdoing to you, such as overpopulation for a specific place. For example, let's take germs which multiply in the body of an animal. If they over reproduce themselves, they kill their host. Next, the entire population inside that animal dies. This is considered as species wrongdoing for that area, which, in this case, is the animal's body.

"About another twenty percent of life forms in the Universe may suffer due to global needs. It can affect a planet, a galaxy, or an entire supercluster.

"These are the average distributions for suffering in the entire Universe. But at any given time it may affect a whole section of it. Yet, the overall is well balanced.

"Even if you think it is not fair in some cases, you need to remember, David, that these are part of the tools to regulate the Universe as a whole. We are part of a huge life who has his own systems to keep his life quality and improve it. You take for granted your immune system which kills every day many 'wrongdoing life forms' in your body in order to keep you healthy and alive. Now remember, in away, the same principles apply to the whole Universe.

"Remember that the laws of Nature are effective for the entire life of a spirit and not only for a specific life cycle. Such are the laws of Nature. Everything in life is a cycle. It might be an unseen cycle, misunderstood sometimes, seemingly unfair, or even ignored at some times by a person or a group. Nevertheless, it is a very well balanced and justness phenomenon in the wide aspect of evolutionary events."

"And now, David, let's take a break, tour the astral level for a while and then go back to your body." The angel smiled and disappeared in a flash.

Next night I glided above the sea all the way toward the usual place. The angel was already there, and with his musical voice he immediately started the lecture.

"David, let's explore some of the other Laws of Nature which affect the destiny of each one of us, including the life on your planet. One of these laws is the law of energy usage or the consumption of energy within the living units in the Universe.

"Every life form must use energy for its existence. The consumption of energy is done in many ways. On your physical level, you humans consume energy by eating other life forms who already have consumed energy as well. This includes the consumption of animals which, themselves, consumed other animals or plants for energy use, or plants which received their energy through what you call photosynthesis.

"Spirits or life forms on the level of subatom 7, or purer levels, receive their energy from the Universe's radiation which is constantly available to them. You can call it a nonphysical energy. It is absorbed through the outermost layer of each spirit. There is never a lack of energy in the Universe.

"When a soul reincarnates into a human body on planet Earth, it gets used to receiving a high energy intensity through the connections with the physical body. When the soul of a human departs from his body, it goes through a process of readjusting itself to absorb the steady energy from the Universe's constant subatom 7 radiation available in the astral level, and which appears like a thick cloud. Those souls who choose not to continue with the reincarnation process feel the need to manifest themselves through a human body again and use the high energy intensity, the same as they got used to while they lived in their own bodies. Since they really cannot attach themselves to the main cells of the nervous system, which are the main bondings to the human soul, they are attaching themselves to secondary sources which are the muscles, fat or bones' cells of human bodies. These muscles and fat cells are not attached to the main soul directly. Therefore, it is easy to remove a possessing intruder very rapidly. Intruders pay the price of trying to use the energy of someone else instead of using the plenty of the subatom 7 energy available in the astral level. They lose some of their own soul energy."

"Are we humans paying the price for consuming animals and plants?" I asked the angel.

"David," the angel looked at me seriously, "for now, until some evolutionary changes occur, it is OK to consume animals and plants, but humanity must consider this: All life forms in the Universe, even those that humans kill in order to eat them, are part of the same huge life cycle to which we all belong. As such, all life forms are equal in their value. They have the right to live happy and joyful lives as fully and as long as they can, and to enjoy and to fulfill their lives—very much the same rights which humans on Earth believe are theirs to have. More than that, once humanity became the strongest life form on Earth, it was, and still is, its duty to keep the living rights of other animals and plants within the limits of survival. Those limits of survival are in a constant change. Humans must observe these rights. The ones who ignore the rights of animals and plants to live their fullest life spans within the true survival needs of humanity pay the price in a few ways as I told you earlier.

"Some people might get the wrong idea as to why they suffer in their present life cycle. What they might not know is that part of the population in the last few thousand years has suffered as a result of ignoring the rights of animals to live as Nature intended. Remember, it does not pertain to the killing of animals or plants for survival, including for self-defense and energy consumption, as part of the long link of the food chain you have on your planet. It does pertain to the suffering and to the hardship they undergo before death as a result of humans' brutality and ignorance of their feelings and pains. It is a sad phenomenon that some of the more educated people on Earth developed such an absurd theory as far as the emotions of animals and plants are concerned. For them, animals and plants simply don't have feelings and emotions. Therefore they concluded that it was OK to ignore their rights, their pains and fears. Those people eventually pay the price, either in their present life cycle or in a future one."

"Maybe someone needs to tell them that they are wrong?"

"David, it is not for you to educate those people or tell them why they are wrong, simply because they will not accept it although this knowledge is within their souls, within their CFs. This justness part within each person should dictate the right approach to other lives, even if those lives are animals or plants. Each one, deep inside, knows what is right or wrong, but some choose to ignore it. Other than for survival it is forbidden to kill animals or plants and, even worse than that, to torture animals or plants which some insects, animals and humans still do. Remember, the laws of Nature are active and powerful. The destiny of each is influenced by them. Because they are implanted in each one of you—and all other life forms—they never forget nor ignore the true acts of kindness or cruelty, supporting the advancement of human evolution or acting against true, loving unification of all human beings. The laws of Nature work in their eternal momentum designed by the Creator, regardless of whether humans believe in these laws or not."

A few spirits in the shape of domestic animals suddenly floated by. I wasn't sure if they were attracted to the area because of the topic that Lamdiel had raised.

"Now, David," the angel continued, "let's talk a little about the life of matter, its consciousness and its interaction with the living units of the Universe which on Earth you call souls or spirits. This concept may explain the need to reincarnate over and over again which definitely influences humanity and any other life forms in the Universe. You can call it the law of bonding the physical matter with the living matter.

"Everything in the Universe is alive, but in a wide variety of life stages. Simple matter is in a simple living condition, but due to interaction with living units, it becomes more and more active in the cosmic evolutionary process. Let me give you an example of this phenomenon. Science's current knowledge on

Earth enables you to perform types of laboratories' experiments that let you 'create' simple amino acids which then develop into simple cell-like structures which are the basics of life. Right David? "

"Yes," I responded, remembering my talks with my father ... but so ...

"Be patient. Within few seconds you will get an answer," smiled the angel.

"As I told you earlier, your scientists are able to use simple materials and process them to create simple proteins in the laboratory. And the fact is that the compound of materials with the right energy and electric current serves only to awaken the matter so that it can then bond itself together in a specific form; thus, creating simple amino acids, then creating compounded proteins, and then—with time—the more compounded life forms on Earth and in other places as well. This simple matter, in order to become a simple active life form such as an amino acid, has to bond itself with an extra spirit, small and simple—that is true—yet containing enough living energy to awaken the life within the matter from its eternal semi-sleep state. The scientists who had the insight to `create life' were right but, behind the technical part, what really happened was a little bit different from their logical assumptions. They assumed, at least officially, that life, or what you call life on Earth, actually is lifeless. That life is a simple chemical reaction. In reality that is exactly the opposite. It should have been the proof that ALL MATTER IS ALIVE! Instead, they choose to ignore the obvious.

"The law of bonding the physical matter with the living matter is a factor which regulates the whole Universe and influences your planet as well. It pertains to the bonding between the living units and nonliving matter on all levels of the Universe. There is a constant bonding force between the living units and the nonliving matter, forcing all matter to evolve into higher levels of complexity and size in order, ultimately, to be able to host more highly developed life forms. It is done in order to complete the cycle of reunification into the entire closed Universe complex. You also can view it as the creation's or the Creator's evolutionary process.

"Destiny laws and the evolutionary process, in general, influence the living units more than the matter, but also affect the way a bond between living units and nonliving matter takes place. The bonding factor will be important for you to know when we will deal with the healing issues of life, including that of humans. These laws are similar for all life forms in all of the ten levels of existence. They obey the same laws of Nature in our Universe. These are the main laws which determine, practically, the way a specific spirit will enter into a matching new body. As a general rule, every spirit has a specific amount of energy, and the new physical body also has an equivalent ability to `hold' that specific amount of energy intensity. Again, David, let me repeat it. It is only when these two match each other—which are the energies of the spirit and of the new body—that a synergy occurs, and a new living form, either a microorganism, plant, animal or a human being, emerges into the physical world.

"A similar phenomenon of bonds between the living units and the matching physical matter from subatom 7 to subatom 1 is actually happening within all levels of the Universe at any given time.

"David, now that we have covered some of the laws of Nature and forces which influence the destiny of all the life forms in the Universe, you should know about another factor that may change all the previous ones. Although this factor does not affect humanity in a direct way, it can influence all of us in the Universe including the laws of Nature. We call it the Creator's will or, in short—CW.

"All living forms in this Universe are part of the Creator and, as such, we must live in accordance with the laws of Nature which are also the laws of the Creator. As far as we know, the Creator has the power and ability to change and evolve in other ways than through the laws of Nature. Within this power, there is also the power of changing events and the destiny of a segment or all of the parts of the Universe. We can assume so, or see it, as part of His tremendous abilities. But as for the personal destiny of each one of you, as humans, or the destiny of all of humanity, it does not apply, simply because you are too small a power within the Universe to create any momentum that will require His decision to change any laws of Nature in the Universe. There is no law of Nature that is especially designed for humanity alone.

"It may have happened from time to time that some intelligent living units did change some of the laws of Nature, but to a very minor degree and mainly on a local base, in a small, well-defined segment of the Universe. The Old Spirits who exist in the divine level did it a few times by creating a more intense or condensed energy space in the Universe within the various spaces and levels where they live. At those areas in space, the codes of evolution did change into a slower evolutionary process, affecting, in a way, all the subatoms and living units within their partial region. But as a whole, the Universe is well balanced. For example, in other areas of the Universe—such as the physical dimension where humanoids exist—there is an acceleration of the evolutionary process so the balance is kept.

"The laws of Nature help every life form to achieve its maximum fulfillment. It pushes life forms to evolve through a unification process which is done with lots of love and devotion for the betterment of the whole. Evolution for humanity means a better life for all of you now and in your future cycles. Eventually it is part of the Creator's evolutionary process. But as I told you earlier we, all of the life forms including humans on Earth, have to contribute to it and then we are all benefited."

The time passed fast. Another night arrived and soon I was floating peacefully above the water of the Mediterranean Sea, ready for another lecture by the angel Lamdiel.

14
The Origin of Humanity on Earth

"**D**avid," the angel greeted me with a smile, "you have learned the basics, but there is still much more to learn. Now you are getting to the point where I can tell you about something you asked me during one of the previous lessons—about your ancestors on planet Earth."

I was excited. I had been waiting for that information for a while.

"The need to know who you are as the human race on Earth has been constantly searched for by you humans. People will continue to look for their roots for as long as they are alive on the physical level. Even animals and plants have similar needs for understanding life though their simple awareness. Of course, it is a universal need because all living things in the Universe have actually the same basic potential for high intelligence.

"You humans have come a long way in the evolutionary process. Your evolution was further developed from your ancestors, the apes, by the alien visitors who came from another planet which is located in a galaxy near your Milky Way galaxy. Those aliens are actually humanoids, like you are now. They arrived at planet Earth on a scientific mission. This was in order to increase the universal humanoids' population on the physical level, through improving the mental capacity of the most advanced and intelligent animals, the ones that are closest to humanoids which they could find. They found a type of apes/humanoids. These apes were partially more developed than the other animals and apes of that time.

"The whole process started more than fifteen million years

ago with the artificial insemination of many female apes with a special modified sperm that could be accepted genetically by the female apes who were inseminated. This process came after many visits to the planet Earth by different aliens from other galaxies. Those visits are documented all over the history of your planet. Earth humans have to be more open to this reality. They will find that the aliens imprinted marks which were left on purpose so they would be found by the newly developed humanoids—by you humans on Earth—to be able to understand your origin and the way you were so rapidly evolved from the apes. This initial insemination was repeated in a few places on Earth and was followed by many other more advanced genetic inseminations. That was a gradual process which took well over fifteen million years to accomplish, until you achieved your present intelligence.

"I am aware," the angel continued with a serious voice, "of the scientific evolutionary explanations of how humanoids, or actually the 'modern man,' did evolve. According to your science, man had developed from the 'Neanderthal man' who, in turn, had developed from a series of other less evolved humanoids such as the 'Homo erectus,' which evolved from the 'Homo habilis,' who evolved from 'Australopithecus,' and so on. But, if that was the case of normal evolutionary process without any external interference, then you would have to find on Earth many intelligent apes and other primates in various stages of being able to reach your intelligence, especially because there is a tendency for imitation among the various species. Just consider this: The most primitive humans, found in the most isolated places on Earth, are but one step away from the modern civilization. As a proof, take any such primitive human couple from some isolated area of the world who never have seen a white person or advanced civilization. Bring them to a place like New York City, teach them patiently and supply them with advanced technology, which maybe will be hard for them to grasp. If this couple brings a child into the world, this child, being born and educated as any other child in New York, will eventually develop similarly to any other person, provided that, at home, he will get advanced education such as that of any other child in New York.

"Then, try to do it with any ape, and see the difference for yourself. Based on the fact that there were many millions of years of exposure to the advanced humanoids all over the world, those apes should have been much more highly developed, if we assume the 'official' theory of human evolution. Basically the scientific theory of evolution is correct, but to a limited degree. Without these artificial stimulations for intelligence improvement in what you call today the human race on Earth, the apes of the ancient time probably would evolve to high stages as a natural process of evolution. However, they would be evolved very much as are the apes of today. The time frame to achieve the present humans' developmental stage would take much longer. Yes, David, if nothing had accelerated your evolution, you would be also at some stage in life as you are now, but only after many more millions of years. You would develop and evolve similarly to your advancements now, but then you wouldn't be the only developed ones—most of the apes and monkeys also would be in some advancement of intelligence similar to yours.

"The more intelligent the species is, the faster it is going to evolve. It is the result of a compounded logarithmic advancement of intelligence which humans now reach by themselves without further stimulation from the outside. Today you are still being observed and supervised by those aliens in order to ensure your continuous growth. The intelligence accelerations which were induced on the apes to transform them into humans have helped humans a lot, but it also brought some difficulties to you as humans. These include partial negligence of the body needs which involves the creation of many common physical and mental disorders.

"David, you remember the night I told you about the bonding stages of the human body and soul, especially that the human soul feels detached from the body's mini-souls, often neglecting the needs of trillions of cells. Yes, David, as I mentioned to you earlier, it is rooted in the history of the human race. It pertained to these steps of artificial intelligence accelerations on Earth.

"As a result of the rapidly induced evolution on your planet, the much simpler spirits of apes could not match the newly developed humanoid bodies. These newly evolved bodies created a new environment for bigger spirits to bond with them—human souls. These souls, who matched the newly advanced bodies, came from different parts of the Universe and they are one of the main reasons that the extraterrestrials are looking for new places—places where human souls can inhabit matching bodies. The human souls are coming from the same sources and they are in a great number all over the Universe. We shall learn more about the human soul's origin in the coming lessons. For now let's continue.

"The human souls who came from the more advanced types of humanoids were not used to dealing with such a massive quantity of cells founded in the newly formed bodies of the developed species. Therefore, they partially ignored some of the problems and issues of the cells' souls.

"So, in reality, it really isn't the human souls' fault for ignoring their own cells' needs and emotions. Also, due to the brain and mind rapid evolution which was induced in you by the extraterrestrials many millions of years ago, and then repeatedly improved many times later, some drastic changes occurred, among them the partial disconnection of the emotional mind from the body cells. This phenomenon happened, also, in addition to the souls' differences in awareness. The humanoid extraterrestrials implanted in the newly formed humans their own conscious genetic code. This genetic code was different from the one on Earth. Those humanoids planned it on purpose, assuming that, eventually, the new genetically implanted mind would adjust itself to the changing new body. From their point of view they were right. The problems are relatively very small in comparison to the enormous cognitive advancement you have achieved. They knew that the human mind, eventually, would be able to adjust itself to a much more intense demand and the requirements from the fast growing, advanced society which it was going to face due to the accelerated brain development.

"The human race on Earth is not formally aware of this brain acceleration, but deep in their subconscious minds they all know the truth. Deep inside, they are all aware of this information and act accordingly in spite of the official denial on your planet to the existence of extraterrestrials or to their involvement in the evolution of your race. A few intuitive researchers and writers on your planet have described some of the extraterrestrial involvement in the evolution of humanity based on the evidences these visitors left on Earth.

"The desire of humans to fulfill their I Factor at the expense of their own destiny—creating sometimes crimes one against another while trying to fulfill their own wishes—is rooted in the artificial acceleration of your brains.

"Of course, not all humans become so adversely affected. Not all have that negative communication with their own bodies, or commit crimes against their own race in order to fulfil their I Factor. But unfortunately there are still many who are inflicted with it.

"David, as you proceed with this training, we will talk more about the I Factor and its relation to various issues of health and healing. You will learn a few natural methods of how to restore the communication with the body cells, also the many ways that the body does protect against its negligence, and how the body reacts in these cases, which for the observer may appear as classical signs of diseases and mental disorders."

* * *

Fears and ignorance were, and
still are, the worst enemies of the
human race. They are real obstacles in
the process of evolution.

* * *

For the entire human race there is only
one way to go—the positive way of love,
devotion, feelings of belonging to the
whole of humanity and being lovingly
accepted by others.

* * *

15
Communication with the Spirits and Guardian Angels

"**N**ow, David, that we have touched briefly on humanity's origin, and you have a partial understanding as to why the communication with your own bodies needs to improve, let's continue and learn about how the souls of humans who passed away can communicate with humans on the physical level."

The angel stopped the lecturing for a few moments while both of us were looking at the many floating spirits around us; some of them were observing us curiously, but didn't come closer.

"Let's continue now, David," the angel smiled.

"After a person dies, his soul leaves into the astral level; the soul stays there for a while until he is ready for his next step which is leaving the astral body on the astral level and going into the eteric level. This process is similar to leaving the physical body and going into the astral level. There are a few differences: The soul, at the waiting area of the eteric level, can get back into the astral level at any time. In that process the soul either condenses himself—which happens in some of the cases—and/or assumes a new astral energy body temporarily. Then, when he is ready to go back into the eteric level, he simply changes the condensation state. In the other cases, if he assumed a new astral body, he has to leave it first, and then go back into the waiting area of the eteric level.

"The soul, at the waiting area of the eteric level, enters into a mental condition which is called `semi-sleep'. Let's explore this state of the soul. This is very different from the sleeping state which you are familiar with on the physical level. The soul in the `semi-sleep' condition is actually very awake. He can think, act and do whatever a normal awake soul can do. The difference is in the depth of the relaxation state that the waiting to reincarnate soul is experiencing. Deep relaxation of the spirit is a very common state in the Universe. A soul can be in it for many thousands or millions of years without any problems. Some of the spirits which do not reincarnate into a life form may stay in this state for many trillions of years.

"If souls who are in the waiting area sense that they are needed, or can help in any way, they usually will do so by communicating with humans on Earth. It is done especially if a family member or a friend is passing away. Also, if someone who was close to a specific soul on Earth wants to communicate with that soul through any means of spiritual communication with the spirits, such as through a vision, medium, channeling, seance board, pendulum, cards, automatic writing, radio frequencies talk, a crystal ball and so forth—that spirit probably will cooperate, and then go back into the waiting area of the eteric level as if nothing had happened.

"Some of the early spiritual messengers and their followers didn't recommend the practice of calling, or communicating with those who passed away. This is simply because if, at that moment of leaving the waiting area into the astral level in order to communicate with humans, they are needed to reincarnate new bodies, then they might miss the opportunity. But that was not the only reason. The followers of the spiritual messengers and those who were in power wanted to avoid the direct communication of the general public with the other side. They prohibited their people to contact spirits in any way, so that they would be the only ones who could talk with the other dimension or receive its information. Therefore, in some of the old written spiritual manuscripts, it is mentioned that humans on Earth should not try to communicate with the souls of the departed ones through the various tools, but simply leave them alone. Since then, the communication with the other side, in many segments of Earth, is a forbidden thing. But, as I told you, in reality, the souls in the astral level and also those in the waiting area in the eteric level are very happy to participate in any form of communication with humans on Earth or to welcome and help those new souls who are passing into their dimension. They are especially happy to help those souls of persons whom they previously knew on Earth. If they come from the waiting area for reincarnation on the eteric level, they will go back there to the waiting area, after completing the communication with those they left on Earth. This is done with no problems at all. For the soul who communicates with humans on Earth, the chance that at that specific moment he will be called for reincarnation is very slim. In reality, this chance is so small that it can be ignored as nonexistent. Besides, there is a Free Will in the Universe, so if a soul chooses to participate in the communication with humans, it is by his free choice. No one is forcing any soul to participate, and no harm can be done to either side, in spite of the many fears instilled in humanity during the last few thousand years."

"Can a person call a specific soul through a seance board, for example, just in order to fulfill some inner curiosity?"

"The answer is yes, David. Remember that by creating the opportunity through any of the many spiritual communication tools a soul may choose to participate by his own will. There is nothing wrong in that to either side."

"But I heard that some people who have tried to communicate with spirits got possessed by spirits."

"Possession of the body does not occur due to a communication with spirits. If the bonding of his soul to his body—due to many possible reasons—is not satisfied, a person can be possessed at any given time, and not necessarily during communication with a spirit. You have learned about it, remember?"

"Yes," was my answer, as the clear recollection of the lecture about the six stages of soul and body bonding filled my awareness again.

"In short, no harm can happen to the souls or to those humans who call them. In many instances, it might be quite helpful to the communicating people, and it can widen their awareness and insights.

"You should be aware that in some cases there is a chance that souls of humans who refused to complete their reincarnation process, or go to the eteric level, will communicate with people for the fun of it. They may trick and give misleading information. It is rare, but it can happen. Those souls usually lose more energy and eventually, when they do complete their present reincarnation process, they enter into a less fortunate life cycle.

"Also, you must remember that some of those who communicate with humans are spirits on the astral level who do not reincarnate into humans. Some of them may choose to become guardian angels, supporting specific persons and growing with them. All of the guardian angels try from time to time to communicate with those whom they help. Unfortunately most humans on Earth block those channels of communication. Therefore the majority of the guardian angels have poor communication with those they help."

The angel drew my attention, pointing down now to a spirit who was floating not far away from us, "David, that spirit is one of your guardian angels." I was excited and wanted to go closer and talk with that spirit, but the angel stopped me and said, "You will have many opportunities to talk with this spirit, but for now, I want you to learn more about the guardian angels and their role in humans' lives.

"In reality, various spirits are involved in guiding and helping humans on Earth. They are very helpful to humanity. You, the people on Earth, call these spirits by different names such as: guardian angels, guides, personal angels, watchers, spiritual father, and so on. Some of the guardian angels are actually souls of humans; others are similar spirits but have much stronger and bigger energy intensity than the souls that reincarnate into human bodies. Yet, other spirits are different from those of humans. These are entities who find interest in the humans' activity on Earth. Nearly all of those helping spirits are in the astral level. The only spirits who help humanity and are from purer levels are those who work for the Divine Forces of the Universe.

"For some of the bigger spirits who become guardian angels, it is the only way to connect themselves to the physical level. Since there is not in existence, presently, any physical body that can hold those larger well-developed spirits, they cannot reincarnate into the physical level. Therefore, in order to grow and gain energy as you do from the process of integration between the body and soul, they spiritually connect their destiny to a particular person's destiny, simply by supporting and helping those people who are willing to accept them and live a positive life according to the laws of Nature which will benefit both—the person and his guardian angel or angels.

"Those spirits do help people in various ways, one on one or many at a time. And as I told you earlier, by helping humanity they grow themselves in their energy intensity; hence, improving their own evolution. If you want, you can look at this phenomenon as a symbiosis between the guardian angel's spirit and that specific person.

"Again David, the thing for you to remember is that the guardian angels can help each and every person who is acting according to the laws of Nature for positive evolution. Once a specific person, or a group of people, is acting against the laws of Nature, by becoming cruel, hostile, violent or a thief, liar or forger, takes any other negative actions, or slows down the evolutionary process of humanity, these negative actions besides weakening one's soul's energy, turn also to a negative draining energy for the guardian angel who supports that person. The guardian angels gain energy to their spirits from positive life actions on the physical level, especially when the positive emotions of love, pureness of intent, and devotion to humanity are radiated from the person whom they support. There are strict conditions required to have the support of a guardian angel.

"Because it is very important for all humans on Earth and for you to remember, I will repeat this aspect: If a person is acting negatively, that person's guardian angel/s, at some point in time, will have to leave that individual, simply because the guardian angels are adversely affected by negativity."

"But how do they help us? Can people communicate with them or meet them personally on the physical level, the same as I talk with you here?"

"No, David, there are other ways to talk with them through the many spiritual tools. People have to be open to the guardian angels' existence. They can learn how to communicate with them, but it isn't mandatory in order to get their support."

"When can I talk with my guardian angel whom I saw tonight?"

"As I told you, David, you will have many opportunities to meet in person with your various guardian angels. This will happen once you complete your initial training."

I then recalled my first seance in Debra's house. How excited I had been when the spirit had been able to tell exactly how much money I had had in my pocket . . . Who was that spirit? . . . a guardian angel?

"Yes, David, that spirit was one of your guardian angels," the angel Lamdiel confirmed my thoughts. "We delivered a message to you that night through the seance board."

With that information, the angel sent me back to my body. In a split second I was lying in my bed, still thinking about the latest information knowing that tomorrow I will get more insights into the ways to communicate with the spirits.

16
The Four Levels of Psychic Performance

The next night the angel Lamdiel started immediately with the lecture.

"Metaphysical and spiritual messages from the astral world have been transferred to humans in various ways for many, many years. But not all humanity is open to them, although some people are more actively involved than others.

"Those who are more open to the spiritual messages and involved in psychic activity fall into one of the four major groups—each is more advanced than the preceding: (1)Passive spiritual readers. (2)Active spiritual readers. (3)The straight mode communicators. (4)The purer levels communicators.

"Passive spiritual readers are those spiritual psychic readers who are using various tools for divination, such as the tarot cards and the many other cards, astrology, numerology, I-Ching, geomancy, fireomancy, runes, coffee, tea leaves, intuitively opening a book, spiritual palmistry, and the like.

"The main characteristic of divination in this group of psychic readers is the use of their intuition for divination. If some spirits do choose to communicate with that specific reader, then they have to do it by activation of the coincidences as represented and available through the divination tools in use by the reader. The majority of those who call themselves psychic readers are using one or more of the many tools which are available to humans today. "

"How do those tools work?" I wanted to know.

"David, this is something that you will learn in one of the

coming lessons. Then you will also be taught how to build new ones."

I was very excited at that moment. The angel sensed it and looked at me with a reassuring smile. "Now, let's continue." He went on with the second category of communicators.

"The next group, the active spiritual readers, is going a step further than the first group. They use a more direct communication mode with the other side. This is done mainly with spirits from the astral world, either the soul of a dead person, their guardian angel, or other spirits at the astral level. These psychic readers usually become the channel for that spirit who tries to communicate with the physical world. They use the various tools and techniques which are more advanced in terms of communication, because they can ask questions and receive specific direct answers. There is no limitation to the depth of the answer. The limitations in this level are mainly the awareness and knowledge of the spirit who, being in the astral level, often lacks the vast information available on the purer levels of the Universe. Another limitation has to do with the ability of the psychic person to perceive correctly the information given to him by the spirit and separate it from his own thoughts.

"The tools for this type of communication are well known to humanity. These include the seance board, the automatic writing technique, pendulum, and the like.

"The more active psychic people of this group are, the more they become the tools for divination and communication with the other side. They become either mediums or channels for that soul or spirit. Some other psychics in this group simply can see and mentally talk with the spirits.

"This is a good way for communication with the other side, but somehow it is a limited one, again, because the spirits in the astral level have limited information compared to the more advanced knowledge of reality in the purer levels of the Universe, and due to the currently limited ability of humans on Earth to perceive accurately in the physical level.

"As I said earlier, there is no danger in communicating with the other side and, if done properly, it can help with many insights and to advance knowledge of the future. Being in the astral level, those spirits can have a better grasp of the future time than humans do. They may be of limited but important help to those who receive their information.

"The next, more advanced category, is the straight mode communicators. This group of psychic readers is a far step ahead of the previous groups. The members of this category get out of their body into the astral level, and then they can talk and communicate on the same level as the souls of the departed people or the many spirits on the astral level. Because it is a direct mode of communication, there is no need for tools; it is a matter of finding the right spirit and then to have a nice informative talk, very much like two people would talk on earth.

"This is a much more advanced communication because the psychic person who consciously leaves his body to go into the other side can see for himself many of the issues which the spirit or the soul describes. Also, in this mode the answers will be more complete and honest, because the spirits in the astral world feel differently when they see face to face that soul of the person who asks for information or help. And the telepathic direct talk reduces the misinterpretations as are sometimes done by the psychic readers of the previous groups.

"Although this level of communication, which has been done during the recent history by a few people, is considered much more advanced compared to the previous ones, this direct communication has its own limitations. It has to do with the level of spirits with whom this communication is done. These spirits are usually from the astral dimension and, very rarely from purer levels of the Universe, unless the person who communicates at this level is being trained as a spiritual helper by spirits from the Divine Forces—just like you are now.

"This takes us into the last and most advanced group of

spiritual communications a human being can ever achieve—the purer levels communication, which is the communication with angels and spirits from the higher, purer levels of the Universe.

"The purer levels communicators are a very small group of people at any given time. They start, usually, at a young age. It is a skill for life, one which is, usually, totally unknown to the rest of humanity. These people, as you know, are those who are being selected to become spiritual helpers. They have to possess specific qualifications, high intensity of their souls' energy, and to be accepted by an angel of a high level of existence, usually from the third level. It has to be an angel who is active in the Divine Forces of the Universe and is involved in the physical level, and mainly with humans' activities.

"There is no other way for humans to go into higher levels of existence without active support and training by the angels. The reason is very simple. In contrast to the ability of most souls of living persons to leave into the astral level at one time or another, reaching the purer levels of existence requires a tremendous assistance and preparation, because it is not a natural state for the souls of humans to be in. Initially, unless that person is actively helped, it is impossible for that living person's soul to reach, by will, high levels, such as the eteric level or the light level, which is the one that the helpers usually operate from. This is the reason, David, that you are still in the astral level and not going into higher levels of existence. You simply aren't ready yet."

"When, then, am I going to be there, in the light level?" I couldn't hold that question . . .

The angel Lamdiel smiled and, with a lot of softness in his musical voice, replied: "Soon, David, you are getting there, but still there is some training you have to complete before that stage. You are doing fine, be consistent with your training every day—just as you do now—and soon you will reach that stage.

"The spiritual helpers are the only humans who ever reach the light level of existence, and although they are the most advanced spiritual communicators on Earth, they usually hide it. There is no point for them to show off. They are active enough by helping others when they are out of their bodies and when they are on the physical dimension as well. During their lives these people, after being involved in various activities and jobs, usually become ministers of some religions, spiritual healers, and the many other professions that will enable them to help others in a spiritual, or what you call a metaphysical, way.

"The only people among the spiritual helpers who went public were those who were selected and further volunteered to become spiritual messengers trained by the Divine Forces of the Universe.

"There were only a few spiritual messengers during the last five thousand years. Only a few of those became well-known messengers. They were called by others messiahs, prophets, or holy people. Some of the spiritual messengers of the Divine Forces completed their missions totally unknown as messengers, yet others were even discredited and denied by some humans on Earth.

"Either way, all of those volunteer messengers gained enough energy to be out of the reincarnation cycle if they chose so—which some of them did—and are today active as guardian angels and instructors to other humans, but from the astral level; some, even from the eteric or light level as well.

"The various spiritual messengers, trained and instructed by the Divine Forces, were trying, during the recent history of humanity, to deliver a vital information which can accelerate the evolutionary process; they tried to inform humanity about the reality of the Universe, the laws of Nature, and especially those that pertain to humanity—which is the need to use a positive approach to unite humanity with love, other than the negative tactics which have included fights, wars, cruelty, the use of misleading information and the infliction of fear in various ways.

"And now, David, let's take a break. I want you to observe the various guardian angels and the way they communicate and help humans in your area. You will find it fascinating. Also observe the various spirits who participate tonight with psychic people's various levels of communication. You have at least one hour before going back to your body, so it is time for you to explore what you have learned tonight."

With this last recommendation, the angel disappeared, leaving me to explore the new information by myself. . . and so I did.

Next night I was ready for another lecture by the angel. Not asking me about my previous night's adventures, Lamdiel welcomed me with a smile and immediately continued with an issue that he had started to raise the night before.

17
Evolution through Love

"The concept of human evolution through love isn't new to humanity. The unification of all human beings on your planet is the step that could bring better life to each one of you as individuals, and to the human race as a whole.

"The unification process of all humans on your planet was never intended to be done through the use of power, force, fear or in any other negative way. Simply because then it cannot be a real unification which should be created out of love. If the unification is forced upon humanity, then it is only a short term, or a temporary, control which eventually has to fail without any benefits to those who enforced it.

"For the entire human race there is only one way to go—the positive way of love, devotion, feelings of belonging to the whole of humanity and being lovingly accepted by others.

"The spiritual messengers of the past tried to deliver this message in various ways. They tried to teach the simple truth of avoiding the use of power tactics, cruelty, violence, fear and misleading information. There was but little success. Unfortunately humanity, in general, refused to believe and accept this simple reality. It was so, for various reasons. First, because the evolutionary process was not at the level where the individuals could identify themselves with others as a whole, or accept the idea that human beings in the various countries all over the world can ever become united without the use of power of some nature. Another reason for the failure in the unification of humanity was the fact that the direct communication of the messengers with the people was poor or impossible. The communication between the various countries was in control of their leaders, kings, or governors who were afraid that they would have to give up their powers if the unification with other countries would occur. It was quite easy and simple for those leaders to prevent the spread of opposing information which threatened to end the controlling era for them. And, indeed, they made every effort to convince the rest of the people under their control to reject all together the concepts of equality, love and unification of the entire human race brought by the messengers. It was done by various means, including through misleading information and the use of power against the real spiritual messengers and their followers. The leaders usually discredited the messengers and kept focusing on the differences between the many groups and nations while preparing their people for wars. At some other times, it was done by executing those spiritual messengers. But since by executions, these spiritual messengers have become immortal symbols to many, they assisted, in a way, the evolutionary process. The messengers accepted their destiny with love, knowing that by accepting their fate it meant a tremendous growth for all. It was also an energy gain for their own souls and acceleration of evolution for themselves while they pushed ahead the rest of humanity—whether they were able to deliver the messages to all, or not.

"FEARS AND IGNORANCE WERE, AND STILL ARE, THE WORST ENEMIES OF THE HUMAN RACE. They are real obstacles in the process of evolution. These two factors are also at the root of most crimes, evilness and the many oppositions to the advancements of humanity. In reality, if people stop for a while and think, the way is clear and can be seen by all. All human beings need to follow their own instincts about the unification of humanity with love. This knowledge is part of the imprinted information in every living unit in your souls. It is part of everyone's awareness. All you need to do is open yourselves to its reality. Feel it from within your souls; feel the love, devotion and belonging equally to all humans on Earth, the rest will follow. And in one of our next meetings I will tell you about the future of humanity and why the unification is an important step in your evolutionary process.

"Now, David, you might ask rightly: Why haven't you stopped those people who were slowing down the evolution for the rest of the humanity? Also why didn't you protect the spiritual messengers who were actually sent by you, or why haven't you shown up in front of humanity yourselves to deliver the messages to them? People will accept the messages if they come directly from you . . . and so on.

"The answers to these questions are not that simple," continued the angel with a serious tone in his voice, as if he were actually thinking what should be the best way to present it. It seemed to me that somehow he wasn't really sure of the right answer. But soon he continued with his self-assured musical voice.

"David, we the Divine Forces of the Universe which are the leading power in the Universe, and are actually the part that reflects the Creator's physical aspects as represented by the Young Spirits of the divine level, have our own restrictions. We cannot interfere with the natural process of life on any level or planet, including planet Earth. We cannot appear directly in front of any person on Earth, nor inflict punishment on those who were doing wrong, nor judge any right or wrong activity. We cannot directly save any human including the spiritual messengers, as you might expect us to do. We do interfere and frequently help humans, but indirectly. Most of the times it is simply by planting, or creating a coincidence that saves lives or brings miraculous events. In some cases, people take it as coincidences or as just being lucky or fortunate, without any spiritual connections to these events. As long as an individual doesn't violate the inner laws which are implanted in every living form in the Universe, as part of the Creator's code of living, that human can have the divine protection which is given mainly by the guardian angels. And as I told you, these angels themselves gain energy or more living units to their souls by helping humanity in various ways as long as people do not oppose the evolutionary cycle of the humans' destiny. You will learn more about the guardian angels' activities, also about coincidences and miracles in the lives of human beings. But meanwhile just remember that although we don't interfere directly, the involvement in humans' lives is so intensive that almost every human being has been helped at one time or another, indirectly, personally, as part of a group or as part of the whole humanity.

"With the evolutionary process we cannot interfere or help directly either. If we would interfere directly and appear to humanity as a major power in the Universe, we would create then artificial rapid evolution. This activity would lead to a conflict with the Old Spirits of the divine level. They do not believe in the manifestation of life as you have it in the physical level. They don't believe in what you consider life as a tool to accelerate the evolution of the whole Universe. They believe in a slow evolutionary process which, for you humans, means nonexistence or destruction of life on the physical level. Also, if we do interfere directly, they might see it as an act of unfairness toward them and then get directly involved as well, creating in this way a conflict of interest from which, as a result, humanity eventually would suffer even more.

"As you will find out, there are no secrets in the Universe. Everyone in my level and the other purer ones knows the thoughts and actions of everyone else. Telepathic communication and thoughts are public-domain in the purer levels of the Universe.

"Also, regardless of these issues, for our own destiny in accordance with the laws of Nature, we must keep a fair balance of activity within our limits. Therefore, as I told you, and you will see it eventually for yourself, we do help humanity, but only in the universal, nondirect way.

"Now, let's go back to the spiritual messengers: If the messages which can help humans on Earth are transferred to them through a human being—better by a simple person as were all of the spiritual messengers in the past—then the messages become part of the normal evolutionary process of humanity itself. Even though we have trained that person ourselves, this form of involvement is accepted by the Old Spirits of the divine level.

"Also, David, some of the messages were brought to humanity by the Divine Forces through telepathic messages or dreams. These messages which have helped to accelerate the evolutionary process on your planet actually included major inventions, new technology, ideas, innovations and ways for advancements in all areas of life, including in the science and medicine fields.

"If we transfer this information, in a noncontinuous way, through one selected person at a time, then it is still accepted by the Old Spirits as noninterference. Yes, David, this way, it is not considered a direct interference with the natural evolutionary process which our code of cosmic ethics, as a part of the laws of Nature, forbid us to do.

"Sometimes the spirits and angels of the Divine Forces interfere nondirectly with some of the wrongful human activity on Earth, such as excessive aggression. They never support any particular group, organization, nation nor any religious aggression against others, as some people may wrongly assume. The Divine Forces are helping humanity directly only with issues of the general whole planet's wellness and evolution, including the unbroken continuation known to you as the cycles of life or reincarnations. In some other cases they interfere directly with cosmic interaction between planets. But again, David, we DO NOT interfere directly with human events, or with the normal routine on Earth or any other planet in the Universe, no matter who is right or wrong.

"As Upiel and I told you earlier, the Divine Forces do educate a small number of elected people every generation to become spiritual helpers within the Divine Forces. Then when humans seem to be ready for advancement, and the time is right, we do train a selected spiritual helper to become a spiritual messenger. Those who are selected to be spiritual messengers get advanced training and learn thoroughly the various aspects of the universal reality. They are better informed about the laws of Nature and about other lives in the Universe. They learn how to reach higher levels of existence, operate from the light level, and visit the fourth level of existence. They get a stronger ability to heal and help others, and also get an ability to perceive the future time current, which means a better ability to see and predict events that are related to the future of humanity.

"David, remember this important fact: The chosen spiritual messengers never tried to present themselves or appear in front of people as part of any particular religion, state or place. The messages were always for the entire human race on Earth. The fact that eventually all of those spiritual messengers were perceived by others as if they were belonging to a specific religion or group was the result of misrepresentation in part by other people. Due to the inability of the spiritual messengers to communicate directly and deliver the messages to all of the people on Earth, the real spiritual messages were never spread among you humans as they should have been. More than that, some followers of the spiritual messengers, who themselves were out of spiritual touch and who would never be qualified as spiritual messengers, took control over the spiritual information, and modified the reality to better suit their own narrow-minded wishes. They were acting against what they were supposed to follow, which is the support of the Divine Forces of the Creator and His laws of Nature through love and unification of all the people on Earth. Those followers were unknowingly damaging their own personal future life cycles and evolution when they took the opportunity to gain a temporary power and control by clever tactics of organizing people around the real spiritual messengers, in such a manner, that they themselves would appear as connected to the divine information, while actually they were seeking power. They filled their groups of people with false messages as if these were the real spiritual messages. Moreover, sometimes they were twisting the reality, changing, modifying and even telling lies so they would be accepted and considered as spiritual messengers by the leaders or rulers of their place. Some gained a temporary personal power and became false 'spiritual leaders' of those groups of innocent people who really wished to improve their own destiny and the destiny of the coming generations. In reality, instead of improving their destiny, more conflicts, hostility, suffering and cruelty between groups of human beings arose, due to the false information given to them by those false 'spiritual leaders.' Many conflicts were created with the encouragement of these leaders who each described the other groups' points of view as wrong and evil. At other times, those false 'spiritual leaders' were inflicting fears, threatening and often fighting, punishing and torturing those who wanted to follow their hearts, to follow the inner factors imprinted in each pure living unit in their souls. People who dared to educate themselves in other ways, rather than the 'official' ones which were ordered by the false 'spiritual leaders' or teachers of that time, suffered as well. It has been a sad part in the history of humanity. It is a reality that slowed down the process of evolution on your planet and deprived you of a much better life for each and all individuals on Earth.

"Virtually all the attempts to educate humanity through the real spiritual messengers have failed so far, but the process of evolution is much stronger than any failure. It cannot be stopped since it is implanted in all of you as part of the Creator's living codes. Now, David, the process of unification and understanding among nations has begun, similar to what has happened on other planets all over the Universe. In spite of the ongoing interferences with this process, humanity on Earth today is becoming more and more ready for further advances in their destiny—for a better future of the entire human race on your planet."

The angel paused for a moment, than stared at a huge, high intensity spirit who was smiling toward us from a distance. It seemed to me that the angel Lamdiel knew that spirit very well. The look of the angel toward me acknowledged the sensation I had.

"You can go to your room, David," the angel said.

In a split second I found myself in my bed. Too tired to analyze tonight's lesson, I immediately fell asleep.

Next morning I woke up into a full day's activity, which didn't leave much room for myself.

The night arrived soon. I almost forgot yesterday's lecture until I met with the angel Lamdiel again.

"Today I have a very important message for you, David. Now, just hold my hand."

"Where are we going?"

In a flash we were high in space. Looking down, a great excitement went through my whole soul. A blue planet was down there.

"Planet Earth!" I cried with joy.

Soaked with feelings of love, I just kept looking down, absorbing the scene into my soul.

Those were moments I will never forget.

"David," the angel smiled as he suddenly spoke to me, but, this time there was something different about him; his musical voice turned serious and his eyes shone as he looked at me. I sensed that he was going to tell me about the future, about the destiny of humanity on planet Earth.

18
The Ultimate Prophecy Revealed

"**Y**ou, the human species on Earth, have come a long way in your evolutionary process and, soon, you are going to enter into a new era in your lives which is the next and the major step in your evolutionary process.

"I have already taught you about the concept of advanced life forms, such as a human being which is, in reality, a compound of life inside life, inside life. Each time a more advanced new life form emerges from the unification of the previous ones. David, let's explore it in more detail. It is important because understanding this concept will help you grasp the destiny of humanity.

"You know that a human being is actually a compounded group of lives. It is built of smaller particles, or smaller life forms, which are your body cells. But this is not the end of the story. Your body's cells are also made of smaller particles which are also alive. They aren't considered alive by your scientists. Nevertheless, they have their simpler life forms. You know them as the proteins and amino acids which, again, are made from simpler life forms. They are called by your scientists: molecules. These life forms are arranged in a specific code, creating the proteins and the living cells of your body which, in turn, create the human body. Again, David, this is not the beginning of the compounded life form. These molecules are made from smaller particles as well—the atoms.

"Within the physical level on Earth, the atoms are considered by your scientists as the smallest foundation or the complete basis of all the physical matter. The living aspects of the atom are being ignored, but nevertheless in a much simpler form, the atoms have their own tiny, living spirits within themselves.

"In reality, the atoms' spirits aren't the beginning of the story. As you remember from the previous lessons, each atom is made of many subatoms 7, which are made from subatoms 6 and so on, all the way down to subatoms 1. Each subatom 1, together with the pure living units in the infinite level, is the basic foundation of matter and life in the Universe.

"Now comes the interesting part of the story, David. If you followed the compounded structure of lives inside lives, you probably noticed that a single person is, by now, one of the most advanced complexes of life on Earth. But is it the end of the evolution story?

"The answer, David," continued the angel without waiting to a response, "is NO. A human being on Earth is not the end of the grouping system. The coming step in the evolutionary process is one of the most amazing ones. So listen carefully.

"Similar to your body's cells, the entire human population on Earth is going to form the next group as a compound new life. Through unification of all humans on planet Earth, a new giant life form, holding a much bigger spirit within the souls of humans is going to emerge.

"Similar to the energy links between the cells in your body—besides the physical and chemical connections between your cells—there are unseen energy links among all human beings, even between today's enemies. The links which connect each one of you to the others are much stronger than the individual's needs or even the individual's life. Therefore these unseen energy links affect each and every person on Earth whether one is aware of them or not.

"All over planet Earth, a growing number of humans are in a constant search for meaning in life, for filling a major sensation of spiritual emptiness within the self. The emptiness within people's souls is forcing them to fill it somehow with spiritual or metaphysical activity. This is partly the reason why people are forming, or are devoted to, religions and cults. This emptiness in the human soul is also the factor which will force them to bond to each other further. The laws of Nature are creating this need for filling the emptiness within the soul for a very valid reason. It is creating the groundwork for the next evolutionary step of humanity.

"Before I go further, you must understand the basic foundations of the coming evolutionary step, so let's continue," smiled the angel.

"In the near future, together with the new advancement in communication technology which is part of your evolutionary process, a stronger, natural need of humanity to be united as one big nation will emerge from within the people of all the countries on Earth, peacefully encouraging their leaders and governments to become one big united nation. The better the communication and computerized technology on Earth, the stronger these energy links between humans are going to be. The improved technology is going to create a powerful urge for practical unification of the entire planet Earth and then official unification of all nations, but this is not the end of the story.

"The global needs are subconsciously observed as a priority to the individual needs in life. These global needs of humanity are respected by the individuals as more important than their own lives. It is a phenomenon that can be seen in all life forms on Earth including insects, animals, and humans as well.

"In a way, it is a similar phenomenon to that of the cells which live as part of a larger life form, which is the human body, or any other animal body. The tiny living cells in the body have enough consciousness, love, devotion and feeling of belonging to the entire colony of cells, that they give priority to the community of cells. The priority they give to the community is so high that they are willing to sacrifice their own lives for the wellness of the larger group.

"In the next evolutionary step on Earth, humans are going to be united to each other, but don't worry, David, it is not going to be a physical bonding process like the cells in your body. It will be a mental and energy bonding. Humans on Earth will continue to live as individuals in normal family formats, similar to those of today, but emotionally, mentally, and spiritually they will be bonded to each other—a fact that will lead to a main evolutionary event on Earth.

"Nothing will stop the evolutionary process, but there will be some who will feel themselves to be very strong individuals, thus not feeling the need to unite. And these humans who will choose not to unite will be left behind in their evolutionary process. They will be the ones who will lose in the long run. This will be similar to some amebas or the single cells who didn't feel the need to unite when the many other cells willingly joined together in order to create much more developed life forms—plants, animals or humans. The lives of these cells have changed forever, They became stronger as a group, creating various new life forms. They now can enjoy the energy of the bigger spirits which joined them in their new forms, have more meaning to their otherwise simple lives. They chose to continue the evolutionary process from their own will, and now they are parts in much more developed life forms with much more capability of fulfillment, joy and continuation of their own evolutionary process which will bring them to more and more satisfaction, joy and fulfillment in their lives.

"Right now, humanity is in the process of bonding more strongly, each human to the others. It is done in unseen ways, but sensitive individuals can sense its effect all over the planet and especially the strong emerging collective superconscious mind, which is going to be much stronger in the near future. Also, the new, growing technology affects humanity much more than you can assume initially. It is going to affect you consciously and subconsciously. Consciously through the advanced communication and computerized technology, and subconsciously through the growing of unseen radio, TV and other wave transmissions which are actually energy links among all people on Earth, thus creating an enormous netlike energy around the planet Earth, bonding even further all humanity into a single subconscious and superconscious mind. This stage is the prerequisite for the next major evolutionary step.

"During that period, the search for personal life fulfillment will change into different aspects, and the focus will move into the higher spiritual needs of humanity. Initially the need to fulfill the immediate individual life and family survival was dominant. Once these needs were fulfilled, then other needs to fulfill the personal satisfaction and spiritual awareness arose. Next it is going to be advanced into the global fulfillment of humanity as a whole. It will be done through the new subconscious and superconscious state—a process which has already begun and is going to be much stronger in the near future.

The new coming, global, supermind of humanity has another very important aspect to it. It prepares humanity for the coming next evolutionary step in their lives.

"Before I tell you more about it, let's review your planet for a moment. Your planet is alive—in a way which is very different from what you know. The difference of life intensity is so big that for most of humanity it seems that the planet is lifeless, but remember, David, there is a difference between the life of an animal and that of a simple plant or a tree. Some humans view plants as living forms with no feelings, emotions, or awareness, because these living forms cannot move, communicate, or do many of the things animals and humans do.

"Now, David, think about it: Similar differences, but on a larger scale, are between the recognized life form of a tree and the planet Earth. Whether or not humans recognize the existence of life in their host, the planet Earth has a very potent life and has its own spirit. This concept is similar to the viruses and other microorganisms inside the body of a human. They will never believe that this huge world they live inside of, which is the human body, has its own conscious mind, has feelings and a soul. Humans who live on the planet's surface are the best proof of the Earth's life. Remember, that every atom and molecule in your body is part of this giant life. Although humans are ignoring these factors, you should keep in mind some of the basic facts about your planet. The major life-giving factors that enable life on its surface were evolved from a simpler mechanism, and now they are constantly regulated and maintained in balance. For example, the level of oxygen in the air, the level of the various salts in the oceans and the constant recycling of nutrients between the living organisms, known to you humans as an ecosystem, are part of its regulated environment. This is similar to the way your body regulates its various functions and the internal body environment by keeping a constant level of fluids, oxygen and the various necessary elements.

"The planet and each of the life forms on it have their own spirits. Earth is in a constant communication with your souls. Your evolution is also the evolution of the planet. The living species on Earth represent its living evolution, but the most advanced life forms on it are human beings. They represent the more advanced functions of the planet, similar to the cells of the nervous system which are the most developed cells in your body—the ones which are the sites of bonding with a higher soul, the human soul.

"This process is similar to the way that the souls of cells united themselves and advanced into the next step of evolution in order to continue and grow as a part of a bigger life form that they had created, which is actually a plant, an animal, or a human.

"Next, the new united or energy bonded humans who are actually the most mentally evolved life forms on planet Earth, will make a further step in the filling of the empty space in their souls. They are going to bond themselves to a much bigger spirit which is going to bond with all the souls of the people on Earth in a similar way as your own soul bonded itself with the little souls of the nerve cells in your body.

"The new, enormous giant spirit will coordinate all human lives in the new complex of humanity bonded together. The new giant spirit has the right energy intensity to match the newly bonded entire human population on Earth. This spirit will help humanity to evolve farther into higher frontiers in the Universe. It is the real evolutionary step that many planets in the Universe, which have gone through similar evolutionary advancements, are waiting for in order to communicate with you.

"This process might seem strange, but remember how your own body did the same. Your living cells, when you were very young, as an embryo of a few weeks, were craving for a bigger soul—which is your soul—to bond with them, to bring higher life into their lives. They needed your soul in order to help the tiny cells to fulfill their own evolutionary needs. These needs are, in reality, imprinted in each and every subatom and in every living unit of their spirits. Your cells made a major step in the evolutionary process. They bonded with a bigger soul which was waiting for its reincarnation in the waiting area at the eteric level. They bonded with your soul in order to create you—a much more advanced life form than each one of them separately. That process enriched the cells' lives tremendously. Their lives completely changed. They became stronger, enlightened, full of love and satisfaction. They became part of a bigger life form with a bigger soul who filled the emptiness in their own tiny souls. They made a major step in the process of evolution which is part of the unification of the entire life in the Universe.

"You, the entire humanity, are going to proceed with it. After the unification process with each other, you humans on Earth are going to make the main evolutionary step, the ultimate one as individual humans—you are going to bond with a greater, enormous spirit."

I was excited. "Who is that giant spirit? Who is the one who will bond with all humanity?" I felt as if my heart were racing although I was in my astral body. The angel smiled, then slowly answered my question.

"It is going to be a strong, huge, high intensity spirit from the third level of existence, from the forces level. That spirit is going to bond Himself with all of humanity on the planet Earth.

"It will create a huge new entity—one that will improve your lives tremendously and forever. This huge spirit is quite well known to humanity on Earth. Many people, unknowingly, already are craving to bond with Him. They consciously pray for His help and love Him. In some part of their subconscious minds all people on Earth already know it. And whether they believe in any established religion or not, in times of great need most humans recognize His existence. They call him: God, Elohim, Yahave, Allah, the Heavenly Father, and many other names."

"But I always thought that the Creator is God." I felt confused now, remembering my Bible study at school.

"No, David, the spiritual messengers attempted to inform humanity, and prepare the people on Earth for this coming event during the last five thousand years which is the time that you started to be ready for your next evolutionary step on your planet. Most of the sacred books of the past did mention this important message in various ways. But, unfortunately, in all of the sacred books of the past, this vital information was distorted for many reasons. Partly it was by the attempts to improve or correct their contents. It was done by those who wrote those books, not by the real spiritual messengers of the Divine Forces. Most of the writers of the past who wrote the well-known sacred books didn't even have a direct contact with the real divine messengers. Some didn't know all of the details; others preferred to keep the vital information from the general public, and still others were power seekers who were involved in twisting the reality in order to gain power of control. As I already told you, there are many other reasons for this information to have remained unknown until today. Nevertheless, some spiritual groups on Earth are aware that God is a huge, great spirit who is part of the Creator's Divine Forces. They know that God's destiny is to be linked with humanity. But they don't really know more specific details than that."

I was disappointed. Although I was not reared in a religious family, for me God was a synonymous name for the Creator of everything in the Universe. Now I felt that I needed to adjust something in my awareness, in my belief system. I was bewildered. But on the other hand, I felt an unusual excitement to know that we are really going to be bonded with God. I sensed it clearly that it was going to be a major evolutionary step which would change for the better the life of humanity on Earth.

"David, I understand your feelings," the angel responded, radiating his infinite love toward me. "God, who is the future spirit of humanity on Earth, is now in a special state on the divine level. He is actually waiting for the unification steps of all humans to each other, so He will be able to bond with humanity on Earth. It is a great event for the entire Universe. And as I told you, many planets which have gone through a similar evolutionary process are waiting for this event to happen on Earth."

"But what do you mean that God is in a special state on the divine level?" I wanted to know, feeling excited, but also confused at the same time.

"This enormous spirit, which humans for centuries call God, is in a semi-sleep state for many millions of years in the waiting area of the divine level. It is a similar process to that of the souls of humans who are in the eteric level waiting for reincarnation. This state is very different from the relaxation state known on Earth.

"It might seem to you, initially, that He is simply waiting in a meditation state, but in reality, God is very active among humanity, helping nondirectly, the planet Earth. Of course He is not as actively involved as He will be once He is bonded with you and becomes the spirit of the entire humanity on Earth.

"The coming evolutionary step is an act that humanity should initiate by lovingly unifying themselves into one nation. Also, in some of the spiritual messages, it is written that humanity should not choose any other god, or major spirit, because it is in the destiny of the spirit God to be bonded with the souls of the entire humanity on Earth. This bonding will replace the spiritual and metaphysical emptiness as well as the craving for spiritual awareness in all of you.

"Today the spirit of God is also involved in various aspects of communication with other planets which have similar superintelligences in them. Each one of these planets has gone through the same evolutionary process as yours, but already has been bonded with a major spirit, similar to the size of God, creating a giant superlife form.

"Yes, David, the main activity of the new, giant life form is eventually to communicate with other planets, and actually to establish new relationships with other planets which have been equally evolved.

"It is similar to the process you currently have on your planet—human beings contacting other human beings. They are able to do so after they became the life forms they are now, through an evolutionary process which united single cells into a body and made room for a human soul to enter into that body. As a body, the main activity of the single cells changed from taking care of themselves separately to wanting to communicate with each others of the same type, as humans do to other humans today. This happens in other species on Earth as well.

"The new advance life form—the unified humanity on Earth which will be bonded with God—is a true synergy which will be much more advanced than all the previous individual life forms who emerged from the unification of their cells on Earth.

"Again, David, once this enormous and powerful spirit of God will bond with humanity on planet Earth, a new era of awareness and satisfaction from life will begin. The emptiness, loneliness and even depression you have felt for so many millions of years, the ones that you have tried to fill with religious rituals and spiritual or metaphysical work, will be filled with true awareness, happiness and fulfillment. These will come with the knowledge that you are an important part of this immense entity—a real part of your God's spirit.

"The telephone, radio, TV and other electronic, computerized communications technologies and the telepathic communications among humans will grow tremendously, as well as talents which are considered today as unique psychic phenomena. Your healing powers also will grow tremendously, eliminating a big part of human suffering. Humanity will have fewer emotional and physical disorders and a longer, much better life span with a more stable lifestyle, a more secure one with less need for violence activity or crime to secure the basic fulfillment needs of the I factor.

"The cognitive intelligence of humanity will grow and further develop, many times more than that of today's mental function, which, in turn, will further improve the technology level. The new collective mind of humanity is then going to leap far ahead, enabling further technological developments, including the development of materials and speeds using the subatom 7 materials. This will lead to new levels of transportation and communication between you and planets in the many star systems within your galaxy and other galaxies and clusters.

"In the coming era, people will continue to work and live as usual. Each person on Earth will still be an independent person. You still will have physical contact with others, and will create your own children, as you do it today. There will be major improvements and much longer free time. Since there will be no need for armies any more, all of the young persons will volunteer to further develop your world into a better place to live and fulfill one's life.

"All of these changes with a better relationship and a higher communication level among all people on Earth will bring life to a higher level of satisfaction, while the curiosity, the ability to explore new frontiers will expand tremendously to farther horizons in the Universe.

"In short, the coming event is going to be another giant step, the one following the evolutionary unification step which the single cells made voluntarily with love and devotion many billions of years ago.

"The other evolutionary steps as a new life form—the united humans on Earth—are still far ahead, but I know you can foresee where they will lead."

The great heavenly music deeply moved my soul with a profound intensity.

"Yes . . . " I answered as the vision of the future filled my awareness. It was coming with enormous sensations of life energy, something endless in size, time and space. I knew, then, that these powerful sensations were coming from all over the entire Universe.

At the same time a strong vibration of endless love filled my soul. I looked down. It was radiating from my giant, powerful Mother Earth as if to remind me of the coming events in the near future—soon the complete bonding of humanity on Earth with the spirit God.

And the words "GOD IS WITH US" have now a new meaning in my life. This is, in reality, the ULTIMATE PROPHECY FOR HUMANITY on Earth.

End of Book One
To be continued

Afterword

Dear Reader,

I congratulate you for taking the important step of reading this manuscript.

This book has probably opened new horizons in your awareness. Now with this growing understanding of the Universe and the next evolutionary step of humanity, our personal responsibility emerges to new heights; we are all equal and vital parts in the unification process of humanity on Earth, leading ultimately to the bonding with the spirit God.

In this process there is no need to establish new religions or spiritual groups; no need to worship new leaders or gurus, and no need to change your lifestyle. You can stay peacefully in your present place and continue to observe your religion or spiritual belief. The only thing that matters is to be tolerant, considerate, kind, loving and devoted to our enlarged family which is the entire humanity on Earth.

The new advanced computerized technologies which include satellites, superhighway, and the Internet communications combined with awakening of our spiritual needs, craving for meaningful life, and higher awareness have become a reality we should not ignore anymore.

By now, you may already feel the first steps toward the total unification of humanity—the links between humans all over the planet are increasing rapidly with each new day. Borders' restrictions between countries diminish. This process is clearly complying with the predictions described in the Ultimate Prophecy.

If you feel that the information you have read in this book touches you, let others know about it as well. Networking is the best way to rapidly spread this new awareness all over the planet.

I believe that together we can accelerate the evolutionary process on our planet so that we all may enjoy the coming event as described in the Ultimate Prophecy.

Are we going to reach this stage in our present lifetime? The future will tell . . .Until then, may God and the angels bless you and the entire humanity on Earth.

Moshé Zwang
November, 1995

ABOUT PALM THERAPY^{SM}

and the book:

Palm Therapy™: Program Your Mind Through Your Palms—A Major Breakthrough in Palmistry.

The hand although a small section of the body, has a relatively large area of representation in the brain. Moshé Zwang discovered a new therapy method to relieve stress within minutes and to reshape the personality through a simple stimulation of certain lines and areas in the hand which, according to the field of palmistry, describe one's personality including willpower, talents, childhood memories, future planning and other brain/mind activities.

Palm Therapy^{SM} is a major breakthrough in palmistry. It combines the ancient wisdom of palmistry, Chinese medicine and healing energies with the most advanced theories of modern science, psychology and success techniques, thus creating a powerful, yet a simple tool for success and self-growth. Palm Therapy can be done anywhere and at any time.

Over ten years of experience in this method is summarized in the 730 pages, 172 illustrations book: *Palm Therapy™: Program Your Mind Through Your Palms—A Major Breakthrough in Palmistry.* It includes case histories, basics of palmistry and Palm Therapy—practical instructions. Also it presents the findings of a unique, Super Hand Meridians System, which Palm Therapy^{SM} and each one of the other stimulation techniques such as acupuncture, Korean hand acupuncture, hand reflexology, and acupressure partially use.

Through *Palm Therapy* you'll learn how to help yourself (within the book's Important Notice restrictions): Overcome stress rapidly; sharpen your talents or initiate new ones; achieve higher learning ability and mental clarity; build your charisma and have a magnetic personality; stimulate your vitality and overcome allergy symptoms; stimulate your ESP and much more.

Although we are equal as human beings, we all are unique individuals with different expectations in life. Since each of us has a unique personality, our goals, needs and expectations may differ from others. Becoming successful is according to one's own beliefs, needs, dreams and level of awareness. True success is not limited to the financial one. It describes one's own achievements in the many areas of life. These are represented by various parts of your hand and can be naturally stimulated through Palm Therapy.

You can learn about this technique in the book: *Palm Therapy* (see ordering information and form). *If you wish, you can also send photocopies of your hands for "Hand Markings^{SM}" of the most needed areas of stimulation according to your goals. See information about it in the following pages, or zoom into our World Wide Web site: http://www.bestsellers.com/bestsellers/palmtherapy.html

---

* Hand Markings^{SM} and the book are not intended as a mental or physical therapy, If such is needed, the service of a professional health care provider is strongly recommended.

ABOUT HAND MARKINGS℠

The Headquarters of the International Palm Therapy Association℠ (IPTA) under the supervision of Moshé Zwang will observe the photocopies of your hands and mark your most needed areas and lines for stimulation and/or correction for self-growth and success. These will be mailed back to you with easy to follow instructions for stimulation.

ALL YOU NEED TO DO :

1. Make 3 photocopies of each hand, simply as you copy a document: palm, back and ulnar side (the side of the little finger). You will have 6 copies all together. On the top of each photocopy, please mark all the 3 copies from the right hand with the letter R, and all the copies from the left hand with the letter L. Place all of the copies in a large mailing envelope. Please do not fold.

PALM   BACK   ULNAR SIDE

2. Make a copy of the APPLICATION FOR HAND MARKINGS (FORM # 50012) and fill it out. Requests for Hand Markings will not be processed without the signed application.

3. Attach a check / money order (If you live out of USA, please send money order, remitted in U.S. Dollars) in the amount of $ 30. Make check payable to IPTA.

4. Include a SASE (a self-addressed stamped envelope) or add $3 to the total.

5. Send the above 1,2,3,4, to:

ULTIMATE MIND PUBLISHER
C/O IPTA
P.O.BOX 7453
VAN NUYS, CALIFORNIA 91409-7453
USA

AN APPLICATION FOR HAND MARKINGS℠

PLEASE PRINT

NAME_____

DATE OF BIRTH_____M_____F_____

ADDRESS_____

CITY_____STATE_____ZIP_____

COUNTRY (IF OUTSIDE USA)_____

PHONE DAYTIME _____ - _____

      EVENING _____ -_____

OCCUPATION_____

I am RIGHT HANDED_____ I am LEFT-HANDED_____

My main GOALS are:_____

_____

_____

_____

I allow the IPTA/Ultimate Mind Publisher to use the duplications of the photocopies of my hands (my name remains completely confidential) for future study and/or publications in order to help further develop the field of Palm Therapy.

YES_____ NO_____

MY SIGNATURE below confirms that I understand and agree that the marking of the most needed areas of stimulation or correction in my hands is for self-growth and is not a replacement nor a substitute for any medical or psychological diagnosis and/or treatment by a licensed healthcare provider or the advice of any professional in any other fields. If such service/s is needed I will definitely consult such a professional.

I shall not hold the publishers, authors or IPTA and their staff responsible or liable for any consequences, loss or damage which may result or alleged to be caused, directly or indirectly from the use of any information / instructions I receive in general and in hand markings in particular. I further understand and agree that the hand markings is for entertainment / self-discovery, self-growth or research purposes.

SIGNATURE_____

(Parent/guardian's signature if under 18 years old)

DATE_____

Please send this form with the photocopies of your hands, check / money order, and SASE as directed in the previous page.

FORM # 50012

ORDERING INFORMATION

ULTIMATE MIND PUBLISHER

You can obtain Moshé Zwang's books at your local bookstores or
use the following information and order form to order:

1. If you order by mail, you can photocopy the following Order Form
page, fill it out, and mail it to the publisher's address along with a
check or money order. (If you live out of USA, please send money
order, remitted in U.S. Dollars).

2. For Credit Card orders: Call our 24 hours service in the USA and
CANADA : **1800-35 BOOKS** that is: **1800-352-6657**

PALM THERAPY™: PROGRAM YOUR MIND THROUGH YOUR PALMS—A MAJOR BREAKTHROUGH IN PALMISTRY

ISBN 0-9645519-2-6 soft cover

SIZE: 5 1/3 X 8 3/8, PAGES: 730, ILLUSTRATIONS: 172

PRICE: $29.95 + SHIPPING AND HANDLING (USA): $ 5 for the
first book, and $2 for each additional book.

(California residents of L.A. County add 8.25%. California residents
outside L.A. County add 7.25% per book for sales tax.)

SHIPPING OVERSEAS: add $16 per book, and $15 for each additional.

THE ULTIMATE PROPHECY™ BOOK ONE—THE INITIATION

ISBN 0-9645519-0-X soft cover

SIZE: 5 1/3 X 8 3/8, PAGES: 288

PRICE: $16.95 + SHIPPING AND HANDLING (USA): $3 for the
first book, and $2 for each additional book.

(California residents of L.A. County add 8.25%. California residents
outside L.A. County add 7.25% per book for sales tax.)

SHIPPING OVERSEAS: add $10 per book, and $7 for each additional.

MONEY BACK GUARANTEE

We are committed to your complete satisfaction. If, for any
reason, you are unhappy with your order, return it to us
within 30 days for a full merchandise refund.

ULTIMATE MIND PUBLISHER

ORDER FORM
FOR MAIL ORDERS

TITLE	QUANTITY	PRICE	TOTAL
PALM THERAPY™: PROGRAM YOUR MIND THROUGH YOUR PALMS—A MAJOR BREAKTHROUGH IN PALMISTRY	_____	$29.95	_____
THE ULTIMATE PROPHECY™ BOOK ONE—THE INITIATION	_____	$16.95	_____

SUBTOTAL _____

(California residents of L.A.County add 8.25%. California residents outside L.A. County add 7.25% per book for sales tax.)

TAX (CA) _____

SHIPPING & HANDLING _____

MAKE CHECK OR MONEY ORDER PAYABLE
TO: **ULTIMATE MIND PUBLISHER**
Please remit in US Dollars—do not mail cash

TOTAL_____

PLEASE PRINT
Ordered By:
NAME_____

ADDRESS_____

CITY_____

STATE_____ ZIP_____

COUNTRY (If outside of USA) _____

PHONE DAYTIME _____ - _____

EVENING _____ - _____

Ship To: (Fill out if order to be shipped to a different address than the above.)
NAME _____

ADDRESS_____

CITY _____

STATE_____ ZIP_____

COUNTRY (If outside of USA)_____

PHONE DAYTIME _____ - _____

EVENING _____ - _____

Mail the order form with a check or money order to:
ULTIMATE MIND PUBLISHER
P.O.BOX 7453, Van Nuys, CA 91409-7453, USA

ORDER FORM
FOR MAIL ORDERS

TITLE	QUANTITY	PRICE	TOTAL
PALM THERAPY™: PROGRAM YOUR MIND THROUGH YOUR PALMS—A MAJOR BREAKTHROUGH IN PALMISTRY	_____	$29.95	_____
THE ULTIMATE PROPHECY™ BOOK ONE—THE INITIATION	_____	$16.95	_____

SUBTOTAL _____

(California residents of L.A. County add 8.25%. California residents outside L.A. County add 7.25% per book for sales tax.)

TAX (CA) _____

SHIPPING & HANDLING _____

MAKE CHECK OR MONEY ORDER PAYABLE
TO: **ULTIMATE MIND PUBLISHER**
   Please remit in US Dollars—do not mail cash

TOTAL_____

PLEASE PRINT
Ordered By:
NAME_____

ADDRESS_____

CITY_____

STATE_____ ZIP_____

COUNTRY (If outside of USA) _____

PHONE DAYTIME _____ - _____

         EVENING _____ - _____

Ship To: (Fill out if order to be shipped to a different address than the above.)
NAME _____

ADDRESS_____

CITY _____

STATE_____ ZIP_____

COUNTRY (If outside of USA)_____

PHONE DAYTIME _____ - _____

         EVENING _____ - _____

Mail the order form with a check or money order to:
ULTIMATE MIND PUBLISHER
P.O. BOX 7453, Van Nuys, CA 91409-7453, USA